D0259532

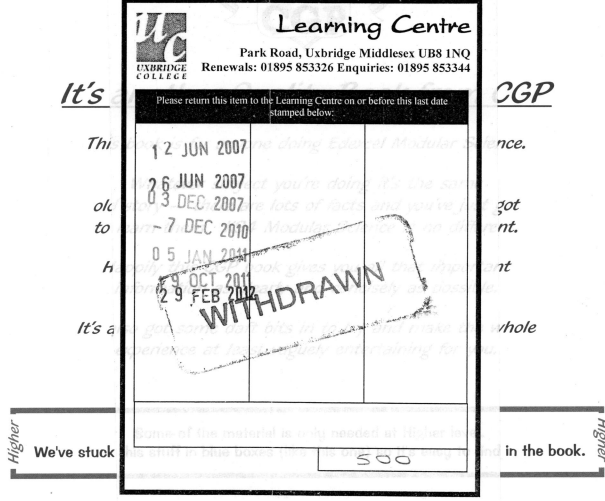

It's about ... CGP

This book is for ... one doing Edexcel Modular Science.

old ... in fact you're doing, it's the same ... there are lots of facts and you've just got to learn ... Modular Science is no different.

Happily, this CGP book gives you all that important information ... as possible.

It's also got some daft bits in to try and make the whole experience at least vaguely entertaining for you.

Higher   We've stuck ... this stuff in blue boxes ... to find ... in the book.   *Higher*

What CGP is all about

Our sole aim here at CGP is to produce the highest quality books — carefully written, immaculately presented and dangerously close to being funny.

Then we work our socks off to get them out to you — at the cheapest possible prices.

Book 1   Contents

Book 1   Contents

Published by: Coordination Group Publications Ltd
Illustrations by: Sandy Gardner   e-mail: illustrations@sandygardner.co.uk
                  and Bowser, Colorado USA

Updated by:
Matthew Ball
Chris Bates
Gemma Hallam
Tim Major
Tessa Moulton
Andy Park
Philip Robson
Julie Schofield

ISBN 1 84146 941 6
Groovy Website: www.cgpbooks.co.uk

Printed by Elanders Hindson, Newcastle upon Tyne.
Clipart sources: CorelDRAW and VECTOR.

Proofreading by:
David Worthington
Eileen Worthington

The Digestive System

The Digestive System

Nine Bits of Your Grisly Digestive System to Learn:

Salivary Glands

Produce an <u>enzyme</u> called <u>amylase</u> in the saliva to start the breakdown of starch.

Tongue

Gullet (Oesophagus)

Sphincters

<u>Rings of muscle</u> which are squeezed shut most of the time.

Gall Bladder

Where <u>bile</u> is stored after it's been made by the <u>liver</u>.

Small intestine

1) Produces the <u>protease</u> and <u>lipase</u> enzymes.
2) This is also where the "food" is <u>absorbed</u> into the <u>blood</u>.
3) The inner surface is covered with <u>villi</u> to <u>increase the surface area</u>. It's also very long.

Stomach

1) It <u>pummels the food</u> with its muscular walls.
2) It produces <u>protease</u> enzymes.
3) It produces <u>hydrochloric acid</u> for two reasons:
   a) To <u>kill bacteria</u>
   b) To give the <u>right pH</u> for the <u>protease</u> enzymes to work (pH 2 - acidic).

Pancreas

Produces the lot: <u>carbohydrase</u>, <u>lipase</u> and the <u>protease</u> enzymes.

Large intestine

Where <u>excess water is absorbed</u> from the food.

Rectum

Where <u>faeces</u> (made up mainly of indigestible food) <u>are stored</u> before they bid you a fond farewell through the <u>anus</u>.

Villi Provide a Really Big Surface Area

The inside of the <u>small intestine</u> is covered in millions and millions of these tiny little projections called <u>villi</u>.

They increase the <u>surface area</u> in a big way so that digested food is <u>absorbed</u> much more quickly into the <u>blood</u>.

Notice they have: 1) a <u>single</u> layer of cells
                  2) a very good <u>blood supply</u>
                     to assist <u>quick absorption</u>.

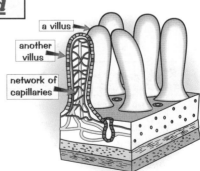

a villus

another villus

network of capillaries

Have you learned the whole page...

One thing they <u>won't</u> ask you in the Exam is to draw the whole digestion system. BUT they <u>will</u> ask you about <u>any</u> part of it, eg. "What happens in the stomach?", or "What does the pancreas produce?" So in the end, you have to <u>learn</u> the whole thing anyway. <u>Cover the page</u> and draw the diagrams, <u>words and all</u>.

Enzymes in Digestion

The Digestive System

There are only <u>three</u> main types of digestive enzymes. Sadly they all have silly names that can be hard to learn and their 'products of digestion' all have suitably silly names too. Ah well — that's Biology for you.

Enzymes break down Big Molecules into Small Ones

1) <u>Starch</u>, <u>proteins</u> and <u>fats</u> are <u>BIG</u> molecules which can't pass through cell walls into the blood.
2) <u>Sugars</u>, <u>amino acids</u>, <u>fatty acids</u> and <u>glycerol</u> are <u>much smaller</u> molecules which go easily into the blood.
3) <u>Enzymes</u> act as <u>catalysts</u> to break down the <u>BIG molecules</u> into the <u>smaller ones</u>.

1) Carbohydrase Breaks Down Carbohydrates

Carbohydrase breaks down <u>long-chain carbohydrates</u> into <u>simple sugars</u>.

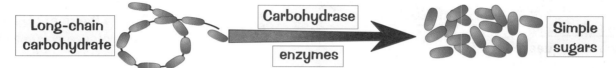

Carbohydrase is produced in <u>three</u> places: 1) The <u>SALIVARY GLANDS</u>
2) The <u>PANCREAS</u>
3) The <u>SMALL INTESTINE</u>

2) Protease Converts Proteins into Amino Acids

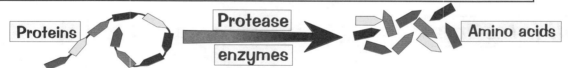

Protease is produced in <u>three</u> places: 1) The <u>STOMACH</u> (where it's called *pepsin*)
2) The <u>PANCREAS</u>
3) The <u>SMALL INTESTINE</u>

3) Lipase Converts Fats into Fatty Acids and Glycerol

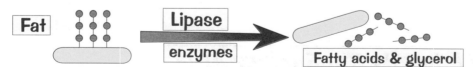

Lipase is produced in <u>two</u> places: 1) The <u>PANCREAS</u>
2) The <u>SMALL INTESTINE</u>

BILE Neutralises The Stomach Acid and Emulsifies Fats

1) Bile is produced in the <u>liver</u> and <u>stored</u> in the <u>gall bladder</u>, before being released into the small intestine.
2) The hydrochloric acid in the stomach makes the pH <u>too acidic</u> for pancreatic enzymes to work properly. Bile is <u>alkaline</u> — it makes conditions more suitable for the enzymes in the small intestine.
3) It <u>emulsifies fats</u>. In other words it breaks the fat into <u>tiny droplets</u>. This gives a much <u>bigger surface area</u> of fat for the enzyme lipase to work on. Nothing too tricky there.

Yes, you have to know all that stuff too...

OK it's a pretty dreary page of boring facts, but it all counts — you're expected to know <u>every bit</u> of information on this page. So, take a deep breath, <u>read it and learn it</u>, then <u>cover the page</u> and <u>scribble it all down</u>. Then try again, and again... until you can do it. Fun fun fun.

Blood

The Blood

Blood's more <u>complicated</u> than it looks, unfortunately. It's got loads of different stuff in.
And not only is it pretty complex stuff — it <u>stains carpets</u> really badly too. It's a right pain.

Blood's Made up of Four Different Things

Blood has four main parts to it.

1) <u>PLASMA</u>,	3) <u>WHITE BLOOD CELLS</u>,
2) <u>RED BLOOD CELLS</u>,	4) <u>PLATELETS</u>.

Plasma

This is a pale straw-coloured liquid which <u>carries just about everything</u>:

1) <u>Red</u> and <u>white blood cells</u> and <u>platelets</u>.
2) Digested food products like <u>glucose</u> and <u>amino acids</u>.
3) <u>Carbon dioxide</u> from the organs to the lungs.
4) <u>Urea</u> from the liver to the kidneys.
5) <u>Hormones</u>.
6) <u>Antibodies</u> (including <u>antitoxins</u>) produced by the white blood cells.

Red Blood Cells

1) Their job is to <u>carry oxygen</u> from the lungs to all the cells in the body.
2) They have a <u>squashed disc shape</u> to give <u>maximum surface area</u> for <u>absorbing oxygen</u>.

3) They contain <u>haemoglobin</u>, which is very <u>red</u>, and which contains a lot of <u>iron</u>.
4) In the lungs, <u>haemoglobin absorbs oxygen</u> to become <u>oxyhaemoglobin</u>. In body tissues the reverse happens to <u>release oxygen to the cells</u>.
5) Red blood cells have <u>no nucleus</u> (they just don't need one).

Platelets

1) These are <u>small fragments of cells</u>.
2) They have <u>no nucleus</u>.
3) They <u>help the blood to clot</u> at a wound, by producing <u>fibrin</u>. Fibrin forms a kind of mesh that blood cells get entangled in, eventually forming a <u>scab</u>.
4) As well as stopping your blood from gushing out and making a mess, the clotting also <u>prevents</u> any passing <u>microorganisms</u> from entering your body through your <u>skin</u>.

(So basically they just float about waiting for accidents to happen!)

More Blood, Sweat and Tears...

Do the same as usual — learn the facts <u>until you can write them down from memory</u>.

Just in case you think all this formal learning is a waste of time, how do you think you'd get on with these typical Exam questions if you didn't <u>learn</u> it all first?

<u>Three typical Exam questions</u>:
1) What is the function of blood plasma? (4 marks)
2) What do platelets do?   (3 marks)
3) What is the function of haemoglobin? (4 marks)

White Blood Cells

Once microorganisms have entered your body they'll <u>reproduce rapidly</u> unless they're destroyed. Your '<u>immune system</u>' does just that and <u>white blood cells</u> are the most important part of it.

White Blood Cells

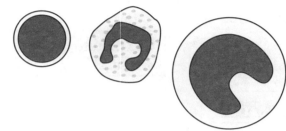

1) Their main role is <u>defence against disease</u>.

2) They have a <u>big nucleus</u>.

3) They <u>gobble up unwelcome microorganisms</u>.

4) They produce <u>antibodies</u> to fight bacteria.

5) They produce <u>antitoxins</u> to neutralise the toxins produced by bacteria.

Your Immune System: White blood cells

White blood cells travel around in your blood and crawl into every part of you, constantly <u>patrolling</u> for microorganisms.
When they come across an invading microorganism they have <u>three lines of attack</u>:

1) Consuming Them

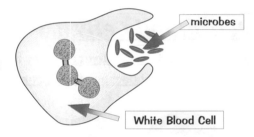

Some white blood cells can <u>engulf</u> foreign cells.

Once the microbe has been completely engulfed, <u>enzymes</u> are released which destroy it.

In effect, the microbe has been <u>digested</u>.

2) Producing Antibodies

When your white blood cells come across a <u>foreign cell</u> they'll start to produce chemicals called <u>antibodies</u> to kill the new invading cells.

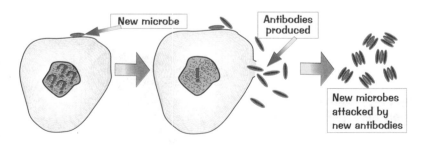

The antibodies are then produced <u>rapidly</u> and flow all round the body to kill all <u>similar</u> bacteria or viruses.

Antibodies <u>match</u> the bacteria or virus <u>perfectly</u> — antibodies for the <u>chickenpox</u> virus will do <u>nothing at all</u> against the <u>measles</u> virus.

3) Producing Antitoxins

<u>Antitoxins</u> counter the effect of any <u>poisons</u> (toxins) produced by the <u>invading bacteria</u>.

Phew — they don't take any prisoners do they...

It's no good just having a <u>vague idea</u> of what's on the page — you have to <u>actually know it all</u>. Learn the three ways that white blood cells deal with invading microorganisms. First, learn the headings, then learn the pesky <u>details</u>. Make sure you can write it all down <u>from memory</u>.

The Nervous System

The Nervous System

If you want to respond to things that happen in the world around you, you need to notice it in the first place. That's why you've got senses. Obviously.

Sense Organs and Receptors

The five sense organs are:
eyes   ears   nose   tongue   skin

These five different <u>sense organs</u> all contain different <u>receptors</u>.

<u>Receptors</u> are groups of cells which are <u>sensitive to a stimulus</u> such as light or heat, etc.

<u>Sense organs</u> and <u>Receptors</u>
Don't get them mixed up:

The <u>eye</u> is a <u>sense organ</u> — it contains <u>light receptors</u>.
The <u>ear</u> is a <u>sense organ</u> — it contains <u>sound receptors</u>.

<u>Receptors</u> are cells which change <u>energy</u> (eg. light energy) into <u>electrical impulses</u>.

The Five Sense Organs and the <u>stimuli</u> that each one is <u>sensitive to</u>:

1) <u>Eyes</u>
<u>Light</u> receptors.

2) <u>Ears</u>
<u>Sound</u> and "<u>balance</u>" receptors.

3) <u>Nose</u>
<u>Taste</u> and <u>smell</u> receptors — chemical stimuli.

4) <u>Tongue</u>
<u>Taste</u> receptors: Bitter, salt, sweet and sour chemical stimuli.

5) <u>Skin</u>
<u>Touch</u>, <u>pressure</u>, and <u>temperature</u> receptors.

<u>Sensory neurone</u>
The <u>nerve fibres</u> that carry signals as <u>electrical impulses</u> from the <u>receptors</u> in the sense organs to the <u>central nervous system</u>.

<u>Motor Neurone</u>
The <u>nerve fibres</u> that carry signals to the <u>effector</u> muscle or gland.

<u>Effectors</u>
All your <u>muscles</u> and <u>glands</u> will respond to nervous impulses.

The <u>central nervous system</u>
This is where all the sensory information is sent and where reflexes and actions are coordinated. It consists of <u>the brain</u> and <u>spinal cord</u> only.

This stuff is easy — I mean it's all just common senses...

There's quite a few names to learn here (as ever!).
But there's no drivel. It's all worth marks in the Exam, so learn it all.
Practise until you can <u>cover the page</u> and <u>scribble down</u> all the details <u>from memory</u>.

The Nervous System

Neurones and the Reflex Arc

The Three Types of Neurone are All Much The Same

The THREE TYPES of NEURONE are:

(They're all pretty much the same, they're just connected to different things, that's all.)

1) SENSORY neurone
2) MOTOR neurone
3) RELAY neurone (or CONNECTOR neurone).

A Typical Neurone:

— *Learn the names* of all the bits:

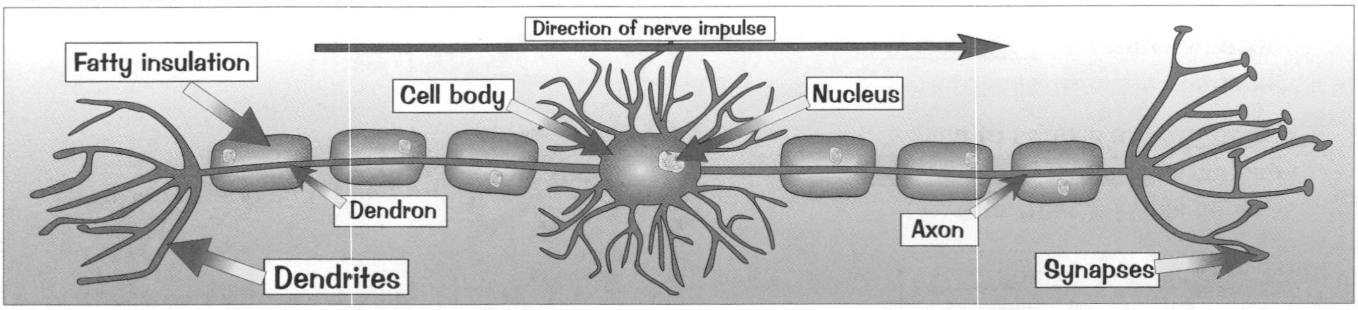

Direction of nerve impulse
Fatty insulation
Cell body
Nucleus
Dendron
Axon
Dendrites
Synapses

The Reflex Arc Allows Very Quick Responses

A Typical Reflex Arc

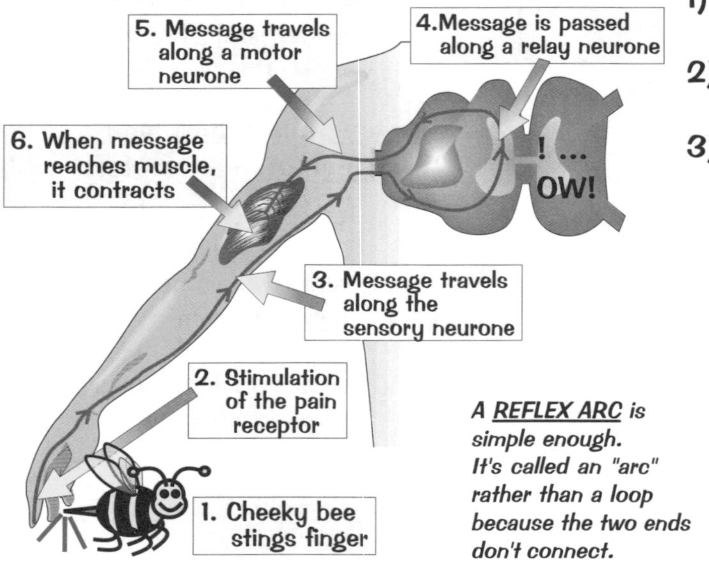

5. Message travels along a motor neurone
4.Message is passed along a relay neurone
6. When message reaches muscle, it contracts
!... OW!
3. Message travels along the sensory neurone
2. Stimulation of the pain receptor
1. Cheeky bee stings finger

A REFLEX ARC is simple enough. It's called an "arc" rather than a loop because the two ends don't connect.

1) The nervous system allows very quick responses because it uses electrical impulses.
2) Reflex actions are ones that you do without thinking so they are even quicker.
3) Reflex actions save your body from injury, eg. pulling your hand off a hot object for you.

Make sure you also learn the BLOCK DIAGRAM of a Reflex Arc:

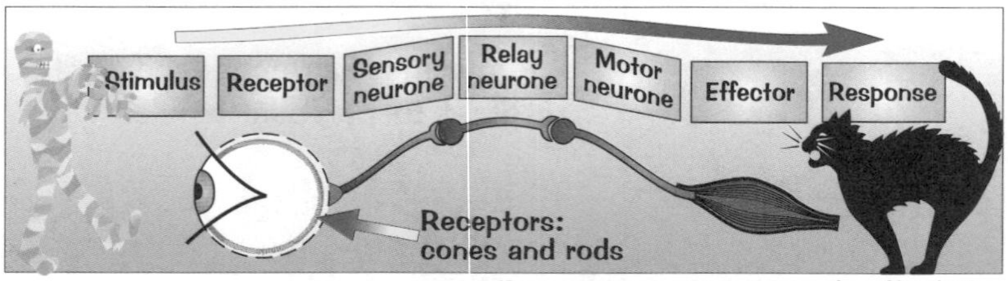

Stimulus
Receptor
Sensory neurone
Relay neurone
Motor neurone
Effector
Response
Receptors: cones and rods

(Does everyone's mummy scare them like this? — thought so.)

Synapses Use Chemicals

1) The connection between two neurones is called a synapse.
2) The nerve signal is transferred by chemicals which diffuse across the gap.
3) These chemicals then set off a new electrical signal in the next neurone.

A Synapse

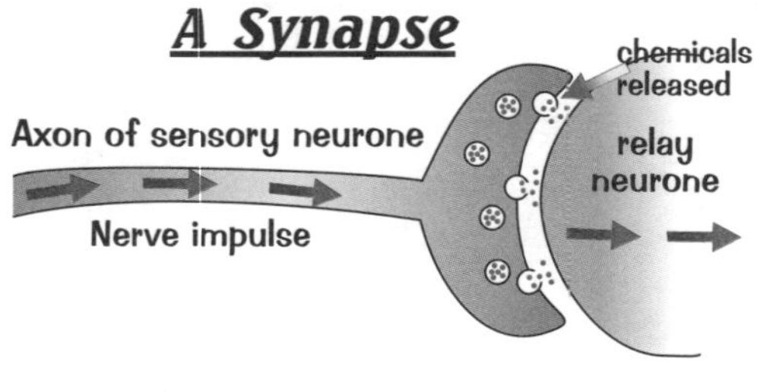

chemicals released
Axon of sensory neurone
relay neurone
Nerve impulse

Higher

Don't get all twitchy — just learn it...

Another jolly page to learn, but it's all good clean fun. Use the diagrams to help you remember the important details. Then cover the page and scribble it all down.

The Eye

Learn The Eye with all its labels:

1) The tough outer <u>sclera</u> has a transparent region at the front called the <u>cornea</u>.

2) The <u>pupil</u> is the <u>hole</u> in the middle of the <u>iris</u> which the <u>light goes through</u>.

3) The size of the pupil is controlled by the <u>muscular</u> iris.

4) The lens is held in position by <u>suspensory ligaments</u> and <u>ciliary muscles</u>.

5) The <u>retina</u> is the <u>light sensitive</u> part and is covered in <u>receptor cells</u>. The cornea and lens produce an image on the retina.

6) Receptor cells send impulses to the brain along neurones in the <u>optic nerve</u>.

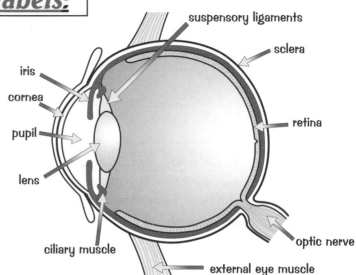

Adjusting for Light and Dark — the IRIS

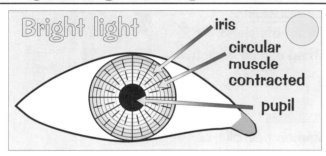

1) The circular muscles <u>contract</u>.
2) The iris <u>closes up</u>, the pupil gets <u>smaller</u>.
3) <u>Less</u> light gets into the eye.

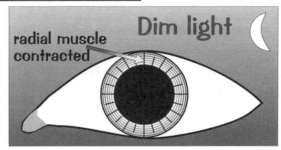

1) The radial muscles <u>contract</u>.
2) The iris <u>opens out</u>, the pupil gets <u>bigger</u>.
3) This lets <u>more light</u> into the eye.

Focusing on Near and Distant Objects

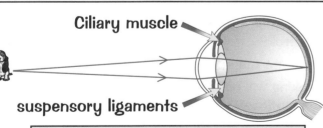
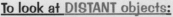
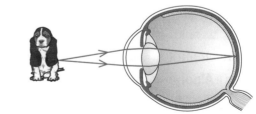

To look at <u>DISTANT</u> objects:
1) The <u>ciliary muscles</u> <u>relax</u>, which allows the <u>suspensory ligaments</u> to <u>pull tight</u>.
2) This makes the lens go <u>thin</u>.

To look at <u>NEAR</u> objects:
1) The <u>ciliary muscles</u> <u>contract</u>, which <u>slackens</u> the <u>suspensory ligaments</u>.
2) The lens becomes <u>fat</u>.

Let's see what you've learned then...

This is a straightforward page of information. Make sure you know the diagrams with all labels and also the points for each. Practise until you can <u>scribble</u> the whole lot down <u>from memory</u>.

Drugs

For the Exam, you'll be expected to know how the drugs on these pages <u>affect the body</u>.

Drugs Affect the Body

Drugs are substances which <u>alter</u> the way the <u>body works</u>. Some drugs are useful.
However, many drugs are <u>dangerous</u> if misused, and many of them are <u>addictive</u>.

The loss of <u>control</u> and <u>judgement</u> caused by drugs can easily lead to <u>death</u> from various other causes eg. choking on vomit, falling down stairs, wrapping the car around a tree at 60 mph etc.

Stimulants 'speed up' the Nervous System

1) <u>Stimulants</u> increase the activity of the nervous system.
   They make the user feel more alert and awake.

2) <u>Caffeine</u> is an example of a mild stimulant. It's found in tea, coffee and cola.

3) <u>Amphetamine</u> and <u>methedrine</u> are also stimulants. Strong stimulants like these
   produce a feeling of <u>boundless energy</u>. The person experiences <u>serious depression</u>
   and <u>tiredness</u> if they stop taking it, so they become <u>dependent</u> all too easily.
   <u>Continued use</u> can lead to severe <u>paranoid delusions</u>.

Sedatives 'slow down' the Nervous System

1) <u>Sedatives</u> slow the nervous system down, and promote sleep.

2) <u>Barbiturates</u> are examples of sedative drugs. They can be addictive.

Painkillers Block Pain Messages

1) Painkillers stop <u>pain receptors</u> from sending <u>messages</u> to the brain.

2) Paracetamol, Aspirin and Ibuprofen are all common painkillers.

Alcohol Affects Reaction Times, Liver and Brain

1) The main effect of alcohol is to <u>reduce the activity</u> of the <u>nervous system</u>. The <u>positive</u>
   aspect of this is that it makes us feel <u>less inhibited</u>. Alcohol in moderation helps people to
   socialise and relax. The <u>negative</u> aspect of this is that alcohol <u>slows down reaction times</u>,
   making it <u>dangerous to drive</u>.

2) However, if you let alcohol take over, it can wreck your life. And it does.
   It wrecks a lot of people's lives. You have to control it.

3) If alcohol starts to <u>take over</u> someone's life there are many <u>harmful effects</u>:

   a) Alcohol is basically <u>poisonous</u>. Too much drinking will cause <u>severe damage</u> to the
      <u>liver</u> and the <u>brain</u> leading to <u>liver disease</u> and a noticeable <u>drop</u> in brain function.

   b) Too much alcohol <u>impairs judgement</u>, which can cause accidents,
      and it can also severely affect the person's work and home life.

   c) Serious dependency on alcohol will eventually lead to <u>loss of job</u>,
      <u>loss of income</u> and the start of a <u>severe downward spiral</u>.

You need to know this — but only in theory...

These are the things they expect you to know for the Exam. Make sure you really know the
<u>effects</u> that alcohol has on the body. Write them down <u>from memory</u>, then check to make
sure you got them right. Don't stop till you've got <u>the lot</u>.

Drugs

The Nervous System

There's quite a lot on the syllabus about drugs and health problems. Read on.

Tobacco Affects Lungs and Circulatory System

1) Tobacco smoke coats the insides of your lungs with tar so they become hideously inefficient.

2) It causes lung cancer. Nine out of every ten lung cancer patients are smokers.

3) Tobacco smoke also causes lung diseases like emphysema and bronchitis, in which the inside of the lungs is basically wrecked. People with severe bronchitis can't manage even a brisk walk, because their lungs can't get enough oxygen into their blood. It kills over 200,000 people in Britain each year.

4) It causes diseases of the heart and blood vessels, leading to heart attacks and strokes.

Smoking Tobacco doesn't have many Positive Effects

Smoking starts off as something people do for social reasons — to fit in, to look the part etc.

The problem is, it's physically and psychologically addictive. It rapidly turns into something they have to do just to feel OK. Thing is, non smokers feel just as OK without bothering to smoke, without spending £20 or more a week and without wrecking their health.

The "best" bit about tobacco is this:
Nicotine, the drug in tobacco, doesn't have that much of an effect — other than making you addicted to it.
You don't get high, just dependent. Great. Fantastic.

Smoking also makes your teeth go yellow.

Solvents Affect Lungs and Neurones

1) Solvents are found in "household" items like paint and glue.

2) Inhaling solvent vapours (ie. glue sniffing) can cause hallucinations.

3) This damages neurones in the brain, causing permanent brain damage.

4) They also damage the lungs, liver and kidneys.

5) Solvent abuse can cause sudden death, either through heart attack, or passing out and inhaling vomit.

Paracetamol — ups and downs

1) Paracetamol is used as a painkiller.

2) Paracetamol overdose causes liver failure, and can kill. The maximum safe dose of paracetamol is 8 500mg tablets over 24 hours. The lethal dose can be as low as 10 tablets taken at once. Alcohol makes paracetamol usage more dangerous.

Heroin — uses and dangers

1) Heroin does have a legitimate use — heavy-duty pain relief for terminally ill cancer patients.

2) Heroin is also known as a rather nasty illegal drug. It's very, very addictive. As the addiction grows the person's whole life degenerates into a constant desperate struggle to obtain money for their daily heroin requirement. Heroin addiction is extremely difficult to break.

3) Injecting heroin carries the risk of getting AIDS through sharing needles.
A desperate heroin addict isn't likely to care whether they're using a clean needle or a dirty one.

Learn about these drugs and then forget them...

Anyone with half a brain avoids these drugs like they do rat fleas.
Enjoy your life, instead of being a sucker.

The Kidney

Homeostasis

Homeostasis is a fancy word. It covers lot of things, so I guess it has to be. Homeostasis covers all the functions of your body which try to maintain a "constant internal environment". Learn the definition:

HOMEOSTASIS – *the maintenance of a CONSTANT INTERNAL ENVIRONMENT*

There are different factors that need to be controlled:

1) REMOVAL OF CO_2
2) REMOVAL OF UREA
} ⟸ These two are wastes. They're constantly produced in the body and you just need to get rid of them.

3) Water content
4) Temperature
} ⟸ These two are "goodies" and we need them, but at the right level — not too much and not too little.

All your body's cells are bathed in tissue fluid, which is just blood plasma which has leaked out of the capillaries (on purpose).

To keep all your cells working properly, this fluid must be just right — in other words, the things listed above must be kept at the right level — not too high, and not too low.

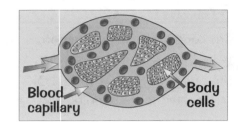
Blood capillary   Body cells

Learn the Organs Involved in Homeostasis:

The Brain
1) Contains receptors to monitor blood temperature and water content and then sends nerve impulses to the skin and to the pituitary gland.
2) It also monitors CO_2 levels.

The Lungs
These remove CO_2 and some of the excess water.

The Kidneys
Remove urea.
They also adjust the ion and water content of the blood.

The Bladder
This is where urine is stored before departure.

Pituitary Gland
Produces many vital hormones, including ADH, for controlling water content.

The Skin
This removes water through sweat and adjusts the body temperature, with the help of...

The Muscles
which can produce heat if necessary (by shivering).

The Liver
The Pancreas
These two work together to adjust blood sugar level.
The liver makes urea.

Fingers *not* needed for homeostasis.

Learn about Homeostasis — and keep your cool...

This is all a bit technical. Homeostasis is really quite a complicated business. It's just a good job it does it automatically or we'd all be in real trouble. You still gotta learn it for your Exam though.

Kidneys

Kidneys basically act as filters to "clean the blood"

The kidneys perform three main roles:

> 1) Removal of urea from the blood.
> 2) Adjustment of ions in the blood.
> 3) Adjustment of water content of the blood.

1) Removal of Urea

1) Urea is produced in the liver.
2) Proteins can't be stored by the body so excess amino acids are broken down by the liver into fats and carbohydrates.
3) The waste product is urea, which is passed into the blood to be filtered out by the kidneys.
   Urea is also lost partly in sweat. Urea is poisonous.

2) Adjustment of Ion Content

1) Ions, such as sodium (Na^+) are taken into the body in food, and then absorbed into the blood.
2) If the food contains too much of any kind of ion then the excess ions are removed by the kidneys. For example, a salty meal will contain far too much Na^+ and the kidneys will remove the excess from the blood.
3) Some ions are also lost in sweat (which tastes salty, you'll have noticed).
4) But the important thing to remember is that the balance is always maintained by the kidneys.

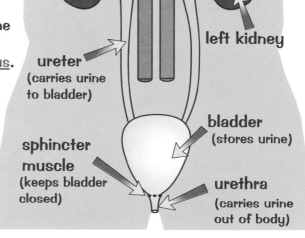

renal vein (contains 'clean' blood from kidneys)

renal artery (contains 'dirty' blood from body)

left kidney

ureter (carries urine to bladder)

bladder (stores urine)

sphincter muscle (keeps bladder closed)

urethra (carries urine out of body)

3) Adjustment of Water Content

Water is taken into the body as food and drink and is lost from the body in four ways:

     1) in URINE   2) in FAECES   3) in SWEAT   4) in BREATH

Once again there's a need for the body to constantly balance the water coming in against the water going out. The amount of water in the faeces and the breath is fairly constant, which means the water balance is between:

   1) Liquids consumed,

   2) Amount sweated out,

   3) Amount dumped by the kidneys in the urine.

ON A COLD DAY, if you don't sweat, you'll produce more urine, which will be pale and dilute.
ON A HOT DAY, you sweat a lot, and your urine will be dark-coloured, concentrated and little of it.
This is assuming that you don't drink any differently. It's pretty obvious what effect drinking has.

How much do you know about kidneys? — Let's see...

Phew. There's some stuff on this page. It's definitely a perfect candidate for the exciting mini–essay method. Learn the three headings, then cover the page, write them down, and then scribble a mini-essay for each one. Then look back and see what you missed. Then try again. And learn the diagram, until you can repeat that too.

The Kidney

Ultrafiltration and The Nephron

(Wasn't that a Star Trek episode?)

Nephrons are the Filtration Units in the Kidneys

1) Ultrafiltration:

1) A <u>high pressure</u> is built up which <u>squeezes water</u>, <u>urea</u>, <u>ions</u> and <u>glucose</u> out of the blood and into the <u>Bowman's capsule</u>.
2) However, <u>big molecules</u> like <u>proteins</u> are <u>not squeezed out</u>. They stay in the blood.

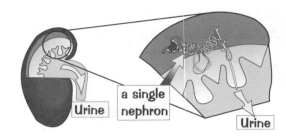

a single nephron

Urine

Urine

Enlarged View of a Single Nephron

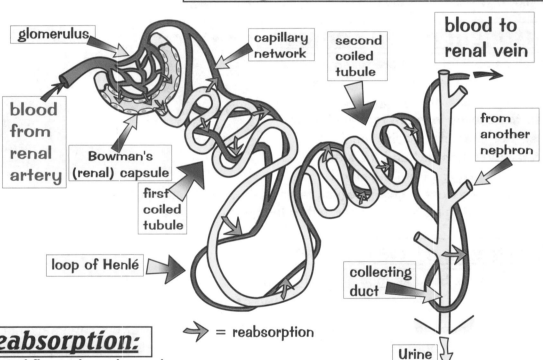

glomerulus

capillary network

second coiled tubule

blood to renal vein

blood from renal artery

Bowman's (renal) capsule

from another nephron

first coiled tubule

loop of Henlé

collecting duct

⟹ = reabsorption

Urine

Urine

2) Reabsorption:

As the liquid flows along the nephron, <u>useful substances are reabsorbed</u> into the blood:
1) <u>All the sugar</u> is reabsorbed. This involves the process of <u>active uptake</u> against the concentration gradient.
2) <u>Sufficient ions</u> are reabsorbed. Excess ions are not. <u>Active uptake</u> is needed.
3) <u>Sufficient water</u> is reabsorbed, according to the level of the hormone <u>ADH</u>.

3) Release of wastes:

All <u>urea</u> and <u>excess ions and water</u> are <u>not reabsorbed</u>.
These continue <u>out of the nephron</u>, into the ureter and down to the <u>bladder</u> as <u>urine</u>.

Let's see how much you've absorbed then...

Do the usual thing — sit and <u>learn it</u>, then <u>cover the page</u> and <u>sketch out the diagrams</u> and <u>scribble down</u> all the important details. Then try again, and again, until you get it all.
I hope it's obvious that you only scribble out very rough diagrams — just to show the details.

ADH — Antidiuretic Hormone

The Kidney

ADH (Antidiuretic Hormone)* — Water Regulation

The brain <u>monitors the water content of the blood</u> and instructs the <u>pituitary gland</u> to release <u>ADH</u> into the blood <u>accordingly</u>, as shown below:

Diuretic just means, "causing you to pee more" so anti-diuretic means it stops you peeing.

Too Much Water in Blood

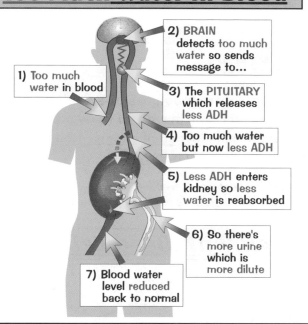

1) Too much water in blood

2) BRAIN detects too much water so sends message to...

3) The PITUITARY which releases less ADH

4) Too much water but now less ADH

5) Less ADH enters kidney so less water is reabsorbed

6) So there's more urine which is more dilute

7) Blood water level reduced back to normal

Too Little Water in Blood

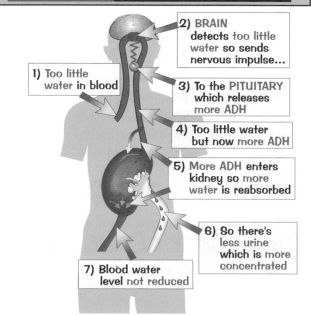

1) Too little water in blood

2) BRAIN detects too little water so sends nervous impulse...

3) To the PITUITARY which releases more ADH

4) Too little water but now more ADH

5) More ADH enters kidney so more water is reabsorbed

6) So there's less urine which is more concentrated

7) Blood water level not reduced

Phew — taking the mickey is much less complicated...

When the exams are looming and you're trying to jam complicated stuff like blood water control in your head it makes life a lot easier if you simplify things. I've had a crack at this one so don't say I never help you out, OK.

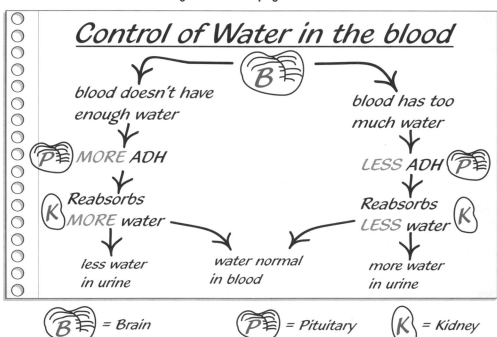

Control of Water in the blood

B

blood doesn't have enough water → P MORE ADH → K Reabsorbs MORE water → less water in urine → water normal in blood

blood has too much water → LESS ADH P → Reabsorbs LESS water K → more water in urine → water normal in blood

B = Brain   P = Pituitary   K = Kidney

Use colours and simple pictures to help you remember what's going on. As soon as you've finished drawing it, turn the page over and try and draw it again, check, try again... and again... and again...

The Skin

Skin

Well, talk about "maintaining a constant internal environment".
It'd be pretty tricky without skin, wouldn't it.

There are Three Main Things that Skin does for you:

1) It stops you DRYING UP (DEHYDRATING).

2) It keeps GERMS OUT.

3) It helps control your TEMPERATURE.

The first two are really pretty obvious. The skin is a waterproof, germproof, nearly-everything-that's-not-too-sharp-or-hot-or-moving-too-fast-proof layer that keeps the rest of the world out (most microorganisms in particular) and so maintains your precious "constant internal environment" so all your little cells can carry on their daily business in warmth and comfort.

(This is starting to remind me of a school, with you lot as the cells, being kept warm, well fed, freshly watered, and constantly supplied with all the stuff you need to carry on your daily 'work'— gee, it's a bit like "Homeostasis High".)

The Surface of your Skin is Covered with Dead Cells

1) The surface of your skin is covered with a layer of dead cells.

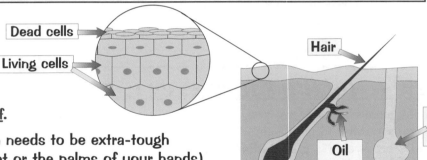

2) These dead cells form a tough coating, and help make the skin waterproof.

3) In places where your skin needs to be extra-tough (like the soles of your feet or the palms of your hands) this layer of dead cells becomes very thick.

4) The oil glands in the hair follicles coat the surface with a thin layer of oil. This oil makes the skin more waterproof.

5) The hairs in your skin, along with sweat from the sweat glands, help to keep your body temperature constant.

Skin Plays a Part in Your Nervous System Too

1) Embedded in your skin are a load of temperature sensors (called receptors).

2) These temperature receptors allow you to detect changes in temperature.

3) Signals from these temperature receptors are passed along sensory nerve fibres to the brain.

4) You also have receptors in your skin that can detect touch and pressure.

I've got you under my skin...

Skin's a bit of an all-round good egg as it keeps you from drying out, stops you getting infected at the drop of a hat, and helps keep you waterproof. So, you know the drill by now — make sure you know all about what the skin does, and practise drawing both diagrams.

Skin and Temperature

The Skin

The skin plays a big part in keeping your body temperature 'just right'. That's because it's clever old stuff. A bit like my cat. Except my cat has sharp claws. And my skin doesn't.

Controlling Our Body Temperature

1) All <u>enzymes</u> work best at a certain temperature. The enzymes within the human body work best at about <u>37°C</u> — so your body has to try and keep things at that temperature.

2) There's a <u>thermoregulatory centre</u> in the <u>brain</u> which acts as your own <u>personal thermostat</u>.

3) It contains receptors that are sensitive to the blood temperature in the brain.

4) The thermoregulatory (there's that word again) centre also <u>receives</u> impulses from the skin.

5) These impulses provide information about <u>skin temperature</u>.

6) The brain sends <u>nervous impulses</u> to the skin to do something to alter body temperature.

The Skin has Three Tricks for Altering Body Temperature

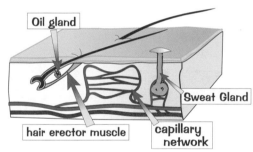

Oil gland / hair erector muscle / Sweat Gland / capillary network

When you're TOO HOT:

1) <u>HAIRS</u> lie flat.

2) <u>SWEAT</u> is produced to cool you down. Sweat is a mixture of water and salts. As the water in sweat evaporates, heat is removed from the skin.

3) The <u>CAPILLARIES</u> near the skin become wider. This is called <u>VASODILATION</u>.

<u>Vasodilation</u> means more blood flows close to the surface of the skin, so heat can be lost by <u>radiation</u> and <u>convection</u>.

When you're TOO COLD:

1) <u>HAIRS</u> stand on end to keep you warm.

2) <u>NO SWEAT</u> is produced.

3) The <u>BLOOD SUPPLY</u> to the skin <u>CLOSES OFF</u>. This is called <u>vasoconstriction</u>.

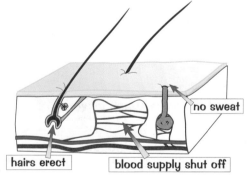

hairs erect / no sweat / blood supply shut off

<u>Vasoconstriction</u> means less blood flows close to the surface of the skin, so less heat is lost by <u>radiation</u> and <u>convection</u>.

When you're Cold your body Increases Metabolism to Produce Heat

It does this in two ways: 1) By <u>INCREASING LIVER ACTIVITY</u>.
2) By <u>SHIVERING</u>.

Both of these <u>GENERATE HEAT</u> inside us by <u>increasing metabolism</u> (ie. converting more energy).

Realistically, hairs standing on end makes <u>no difference</u> to humans. It's a leftover from when we had hairy bodies. However, <u>in your Exam</u> you'll dutifully mention it <u>to get the marks</u>.

These days we just put <u>more layers of clothes on</u>, to trap <u>more layers of air</u>, because <u>air acts as an insulator</u> so long as it's <u>trapped</u> and can't move around — <u>LEARN</u> those details.

Skin and bear it — it's almost over...

I've said it before, and I'll say it again... the <u>best way</u> to fix all this stuff in your head is to learn it, then <u>cover the page</u> and <u>scribble it all down</u> until you make no mistakes <u>at all</u>. And when it comes to diagrams, <u>rough sketches</u> are fine — you don't need works of art. Obvious really.

Revision Summary for Module One

Phew, there's a lot of stuff to learn in Module One. Some of it can be really quite hard to understand. But you have to know it, even if you don't understand it. It's all worth points in the Exam. These questions are designed to test what you know. Keep practising till you can whizz them all off without a moment's hesitation on any of them. It's a nice trick if you can do it.

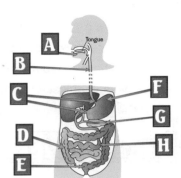

1) Sketch the diagram on the right, adding the names for parts A to H.
2) Where is most water absorbed from food?
3) Sketch a villus, and say what it's for. Label the main features of villi.
4) What *exactly* do enzymes do in the digestive system?
5) List the three main types of digestive enzymes and say which foods they act on.
6) Where is bile produced and stored? What does it do?
7) Sketch a red blood cell and a white blood cell. Give 3 details about each.
8) List all the things that are carried in the blood plasma.
9) Sketch some platelets. What do they do all day?
10) List the three ways that white blood cells deal with invading microorganisms.
11) Name the five sense organs and the stimuli that each one is sensitive to.
12) Sketch and label this diagram of a typical neurone:

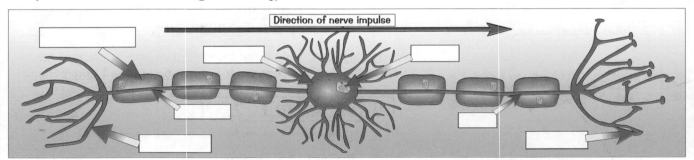

Direction of nerve impulse

13) Describe how a reflex arc works and say why it's a good thing. Explain how a synapse works.
14) Draw a full diagram of an eye with all labels and details.
15) Describe how the eye adjusts for light and dark, and to focus on near and distant objects.
16) What is the difference between stimulants and sedatives? Give an example of each.
17) List three ways that alcohol affects the body.
18) Give three ways in which tobacco smoke affects the lungs.
19) What harm do solvents cause to the body?
20) What type of drug is paracetamol, and what is it used for? Can you overdose on it?
21) Is there a legal, medical use for heroin?
22) What is homeostasis? List two bodily levels which need to be kept constant.
23) What is the basic function of a kidney? What three particular things do they deal with?
24) Describe how urea is removed by the body. Draw and label a diagram showing a single nephron.
25) Draw diagrams to explain how ADH is involved in regulating the water content of the blood.
26) How does our skin let us know what we are touching, or how hot we are?
27) What temperature do the enzymes in our body prefer?
28) What does the skin do when we're a) too hot b) too cold?
29) What are vasoconstriction and vasodilation? How does vasodilation remove heat from the body?
30) Why do we shiver? How does this increase the temperature of the body?

Genes, Chromosomes and DNA

Chromosomes and Variation

If you're going to get <u>anywhere</u> with this topic you definitely need to learn these confusing words and exactly what they mean. <u>You have to make sure you know</u> exactly what <u>DNA</u> is, what and where <u>chromosomes</u> are, and what and where a <u>gene</u> is. If you don't get that sorted out first, then anything else you read about them won't make a lot of sense to you — <u>will it</u>.

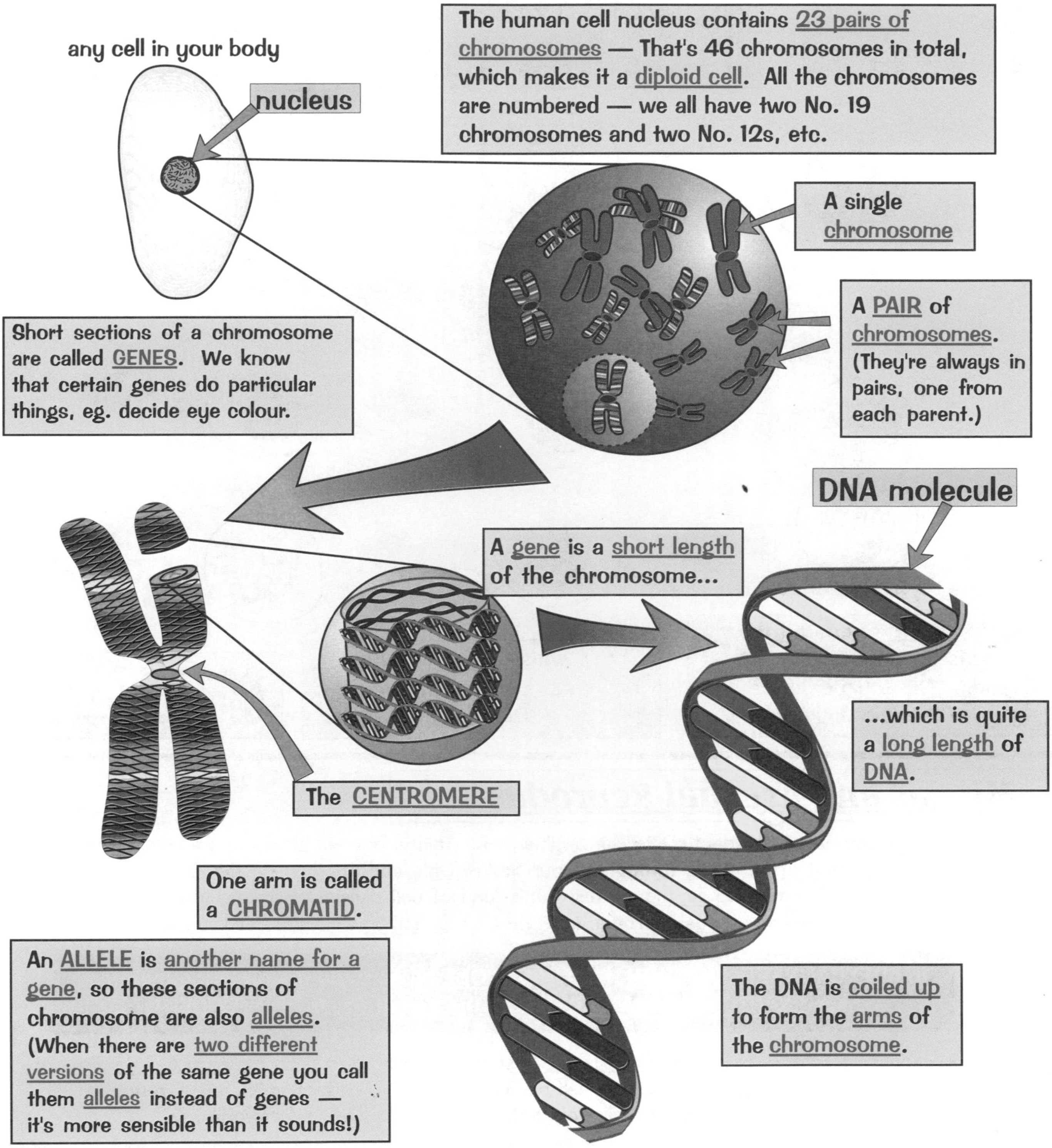

any cell in your body

nucleus

The human cell nucleus contains <u>23 pairs of</u> <u>chromosomes</u> — That's 46 chromosomes in total, which makes it a <u>diploid cell</u>. All the chromosomes are numbered — we all have two No. 19 chromosomes and two No. 12s, etc.

A single <u>chromosome</u>

A <u>PAIR</u> of <u>chromosomes</u>. (They're always in pairs, one from each parent.)

Short sections of a chromosome are called <u>GENES</u>. We know that certain genes do particular things, eg. decide eye colour.

DNA molecule

A <u>gene</u> is a <u>short length</u> of the chromosome...

...which is quite a <u>long length</u> of <u>DNA</u>.

The <u>CENTROMERE</u>

One arm is called a <u>CHROMATID</u>.

The DNA is <u>coiled up</u> to form the <u>arms</u> of the <u>chromosome</u>.

An <u>ALLELE</u> is <u>another name for a</u> <u>gene</u>, so these sections of chromosome are also <u>alleles</u>. (When there are <u>two different</u> <u>versions</u> of the same gene you call them <u>alleles</u> instead of genes — it's more sensible than it sounds!)

Hard Learning? — don't blow it all out of proportion...

This is a real easy page to learn, don't you think. Why, you could learn the whole thing with both ears tied behind your head. <u>Cover the page</u> and <u>scribble down</u> all the diagrams and details.

18

Ordinary Cell Division: Mitosis

"**MITOSIS** is when a cell reproduces itself __ASEXUALLY__ by splitting to form
two identical offspring that are called clones."

DNA all spread out in long strings.

DNA forms into chromosomes. The double arms are already duplicates of each other — remember that.

Chromosomes line up along the centre and then the cell fibres pull them apart.

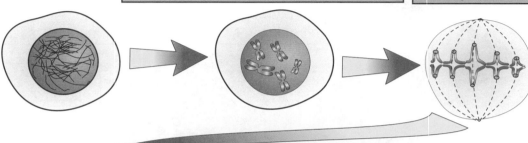

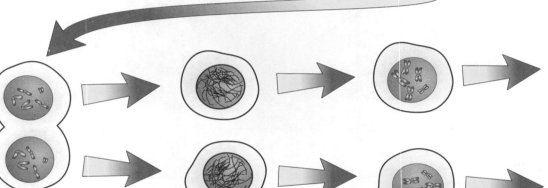

Membranes form around the two sets of chromosome threads. These become the nuclei of the two daughter cells.

The threads unwind into long strands of DNA and the whole process then starts over again.

(Note that the single chromosome threads have now duplicated themselves.)

Mitosis and Asexual Reproduction

Mitosis produces new cells identical to the original cell. This is how all plants and animals grow and produce replacement cells. Cells throughout our body divide and multiply by this process. However some organisms also reproduce using this kind of cell division, bacteria being a good example. This is known as asexual reproduction. Here's a definition of it you need to learn:

In **ASEXUAL REPRODUCTION** there is only **ONE** parent, and the offspring therefore have **EXACTLY THE SAME GENES** as the parent (ie. they're CLONES).

This is because all the cells in both parent and offspring were produced by ordinary cell division, so they must all have identical genes in their cell nuclei. Asexual reproduction therefore produces no variation. Some plants reproduce asexually, eg. potatoes, strawberries and daffodils.

Now that I have your undivided attention...

You need to learn the definition of mitosis, the sequence of diagrams, and also the definition of asexual reproduction. Now cover the page , scribble down the two definitions, and sketch out the sequence of diagrams — don't waste time with neatness — just find out if you've learnt it all yet.

Gamete Production: Meiosis

You thought mitosis was exciting. Hah! You ain't seen nothing yet. <u>Meiosis</u> is the other type of cell division. It only happens in the <u>reproductive organs</u> (ovaries and testes).

> <u>MEIOSIS</u> produces "<u>cells which have half the proper number of chromosomes</u>".
> Such cells are also known as "<u>haploid gametes</u>".

These cells are "genetically different" from each other because the genes all get <u>shuffled up</u> during meiosis and each gamete only gets <u>half of them</u>, selected at random.
Confused? I'm not surprised. But fear not, my little yellow friend...
The diagrams below will make it a lot clearer — but you have to <u>study</u> them pretty hard.

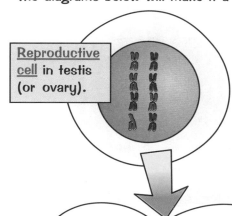

<u>Reproductive cell</u> in testis (or ovary).

1) Remember, there are <u>23 pairs</u> of chromosomes at the start, so that's 46 altogether. This means the cell is a <u>diploid cell</u>. In each <u>pair of chromosomes</u>, there's one you got from your <u>father</u>, and one you got from your <u>mother</u>.

<u>Both</u> chromosomes have information about the <u>same aspects</u> of your body, eg. hair colour, eye colour, etc., but one has information brought from your father (shown red) and one has information from your mother (shown blue). Note the little red <u>y-chromosome</u>.

2) <u>The pairs now split up</u> so that some of your father's chromosomes go with some of your mother's chromosomes, but there'll be <u>no pairs at all now</u>. There'll be just <u>one of each</u> of the 23 different types of chromosomes in each of the two new cells.
   Each cell therefore has a <u>mixture</u> of your mother's and father's characteristics, but only has <u>half the full complement</u> of chromosomes.

3) These cells now split <u>mitosis-style</u>, with the <u>chromosomes themselves splitting</u> to form two identical cells, called <u>gametes</u>. The twin-armed chromosomes were already duplicates, don't forget.

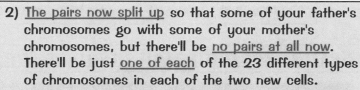
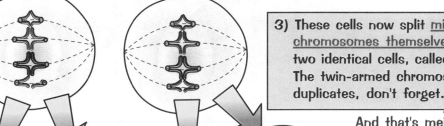

<u>And that's meiosis done</u>.
Note the difference between the <u>first stage</u> where the <u>pairs separate</u> and the <u>second stage</u> where the <u>chromosomes themselves split</u>. It's tricky!

<u>Gametes</u>
ie. sperm cells or egg cells (another name for an egg cell is <u>ovum</u>).

Meiosis? Not even remotely scary...

There's a few tricky words in there which don't help — especially if you just ignore them...
The only way to <u>learn</u> this page is by constant reference to the diagram. Make sure you can sketch all the parts of it <u>from memory</u> and <u>scribble notes</u> to explain each stage.

Fertilisation

Right, here we go again with gametes and all the nonsense that goes with them.
But don't despair, at least this page is easier than the last one.

Reproductive Cells undergo Meiosis to Produce Gametes:

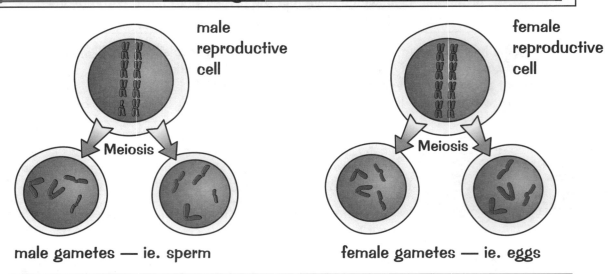

male reproductive cell

female reproductive cell

Meiosis

Meiosis

male gametes — ie. sperm

female gametes — ie. eggs

> The gametes, remember, only have one chromosome to describe each bit of you, one copy of each of the chromosomes numbered 1 to 23. But a normal cell needs two chromosomes of each type — one from each parent, so...

Sexual Reproduction involves the Meeting of Gametes

> Sexual reproduction involves the fusion of male and female gametes (sex cells). Because there are two parents, the offspring contain a mixture of their parents' genes.

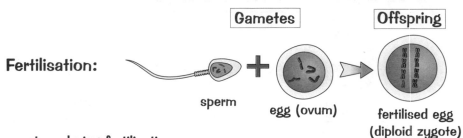

Gametes

Offspring

Fertilisation:

sperm

egg (ovum)

fertilised egg
(diploid zygote)

1) Gametes meet up during fertilisation.

2) The 23 single chromosomes in one gamete all pair off with their appropriate "partner chromosomes" from the other gamete to form the full 23 pairs again, No.4 with No.4, No.13 with No.13 etc. The result of this is a diploid zygote — which is just a fancy way of saying a fertilised egg (ovum).

3) Don't forget, the two chromosomes in a pair both contain the same basic genes, eg. for hair colour, etc. That's why the chromosomes need to pair off.

4) The offspring will receive its outward characteristics as a mixture from the two sets of chromosomes, so it will inherit features from both parents. This is why sexual reproduction produces more variation than asexual reproduction. Pretty cool, eh.

It should all be starting to come together now...

If you go through these last two pages you should see how the two processes, meiosis and fertilisation, are kind of opposite. Practise sketching out the sequence of diagrams, with notes, for both pages till it all sinks in. Nice, innit.

X and Y Chromosomes

There are <u>23 matched pairs</u> of chromosomes in every human body cell. The 23rd pair are labelled XY. They're the two chromosomes that <u>decide whether you turn out male or female</u>. They're called the X and Y chromosomes because they look like an X and a Y.

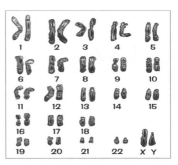

> <u>All MEN</u> have an <u>X</u> and a <u>Y</u> chromosome: XY
> The <u>Y chromosome</u> contains genes that cause <u>MALE characteristics</u>.
>
> <u>All WOMEN</u> have <u>two X chromosomes</u>: XX
> The **XX** combination allows <u>FEMALE characteristics</u> to develop.

The diagram below shows the way the male XY chromosomes and female XX chromosomes <u>split up to form the gametes</u> (ovum or sperm), and then <u>combine together at fertilisation</u>.
The criss-cross lines show all the <u>possible</u> ways the X and Y chromosomes <u>could</u> combine.
Remember, <u>only one of these</u> would actually happen for any offspring.
What the diagram shows us is the <u>relative probability</u> of each type of zygote (offspring) occurring.

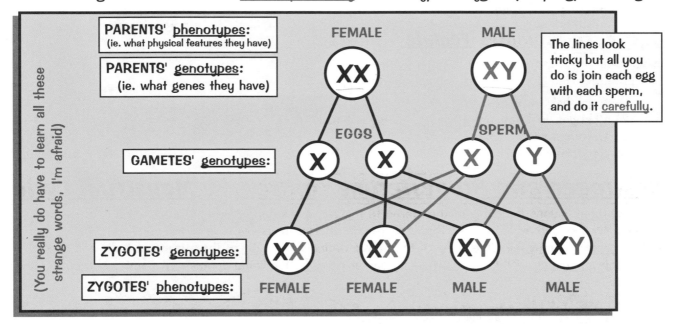

The other way of doing this is with a <u>chequerboard</u> type diagram. If you don't understand how it works, ask your teacher to explain it. The <u>pairs of letters</u> in the middle show the <u>gene types</u> of the possible offspring.

Both diagrams show that there'll be the <u>same proportion</u> of <u>male and female offspring</u>, because there are <u>two XX results</u> and <u>two XY results</u>.

Don't forget though that this <u>50:50 ratio</u> is only a <u>probability</u>. If you had four kids they <u>could</u> all be <u>boys</u> — yes I know, terrifying isn't it.

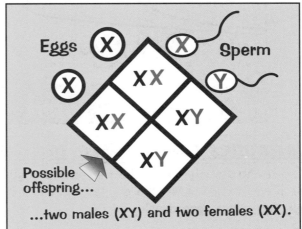

...two males (XY) and two females (XX).

How can it take all that just to say it's a 50:50 chance...

Make sure you know all about X and Y chromosomes and who has what combination.
The diagrams are real important. Practise reproducing them until you can do it <u>effortlessly</u>.

Male and Female Hormones

Hormones are chemical messengers released into the blood from glands.
They travel all over the body in the bloodstream, but they only affect certain cells.

Hormones _Promote_ Sexual Characteristics _at Puberty_

Sex is decided at <u>fertilisation</u>, but it's only when you get to <u>puberty</u> that some of the <u>sexual characteristics</u> of men and women (breasts, body hair, voice pitch) appear.

At puberty your body starts releasing <u>sex hormones</u> (<u>testosterone</u> in men, <u>oestrogen</u> in women). These trigger off the <u>secondary sexual characteristics</u>.

Testosterone _Promotes_ Male _Characteristics_

In males, the testes start producing <u>testosterone</u> at puberty.
This promotes <u>male secondary sexual characteristics</u>:

1) <u>Extra hair</u> in places.
2) Changes in body <u>proportions</u> — bigger muscles.
3) <u>Sperm</u> production.
4) Deepening of <u>voice</u>.

Oestrogen _Promotes_ Female _Characteristics_

In females, the ovaries start producing <u>oestrogen</u> at puberty.
This promotes <u>female secondary sexual characteristics</u>:

1) <u>Extra hair</u> in places.
2) Changes in body <u>proportions</u> — bigger hips.
3) Development of <u>breasts</u>.
4) <u>Egg</u> production.

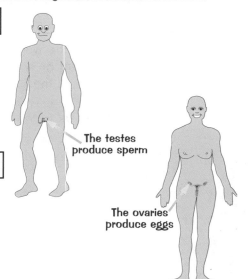

The testes produce sperm

The ovaries produce eggs

Oestrogen _and_ Progesterone _control the_ Menstrual Cycle

1) <u>Oestrogen</u> causes the lining of the uterus to <u>thicken</u> in the <u>early part</u> of the menstrual cycle — after the menstrual period. This <u>prepares</u> the uterus to receive a <u>fertilised egg</u>.

2) <u>Progesterone</u> <u>maintains</u> the lining of the uterus during the <u>middle</u> of the menstrual cycle and during <u>pregnancy</u>. When the level of progesterone <u>falls</u>, the lining <u>breaks down</u> and is shed.

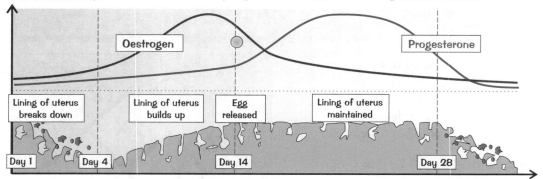

Oestrogen

Progesterone

| Lining of uterus breaks down | Lining of uterus builds up | Egg released | Lining of uterus maintained |

Day 1   Day 4   Day 14   Day 28

Hormones _can be_ Used _to_ Treat _Infertility_

Women who are <u>infertile</u> can be treated with a <u>synthetic version</u> of a <u>hormone</u> called <u>FSH</u>.
This hormone stimulates the <u>ovaries</u> and causes an <u>egg</u> to <u>develop</u>. If the dosage is too high, <u>too many eggs</u> develop at once — causing <u>multiple births</u>.

Hormones — easy peasy...

Make sure you know what <u>all</u> the different hormones do — that includes learning which hormones start off the development of secondary sexual characteristics, and the roles of oestrogen and progesterone in the menstrual cycle. Oh, and learn about fertility treatment too.

Variation

Genes and Variation

The word 'VARIATION' sounds far too fancy for its own good.
All it means is how animals or plants of the same species <u>look or behave slightly differently</u> <u>from each other</u>. You know, a bit <u>taller</u> or a bit <u>fatter</u> or a bit more <u>scary-to-look-at</u> etc.
There are <u>two</u> causes of variation: <u>Genetic variation</u> and <u>Environmental variation</u>. Read on...

1) *Genetic Variation is caused by Genes (surprise)*

All animals, including humans, are bound to be <u>slightly different</u> from each other because their <u>genes</u> are slightly different. Genes are the code which determines how your body turns out. Each gene controls a single <u>inherited</u> <u>trait</u> — eg. <u>eye colour</u>. We all end up with a <u>slightly different</u> set of genes.

The <u>exceptions</u> to this rule are <u>identical twins</u>, because their genes are <u>exactly the same</u>.
But even identical twins are never <u>completely identical</u> — and that's because of the other factor:

2) *Environmental Variation is shown up by Twins*

If you're not sure what "<u>environment</u>" means, think of it as "<u>upbringing</u>" instead
— it's pretty much the same thing — how and where you were "brought up".

Since we know the <u>twins' genes</u> are <u>identical</u>, any differences between them
<u>must</u> be caused by slight differences <u>in their environment</u> throughout their lives.

<u>Twins</u> give us a fairly good idea of how important the
<u>two factors</u> (genes and environment) are, <u>compared to each</u>
<u>other</u> — at least for animals. Plants always show <u>much greater</u>
<u>variation</u> due to differences in their environment than animals do.

Most Variation in Animals is a Mixture

Most variation in animals is caused by a <u>mixture</u> of genetic and environmental factors.
Almost every single aspect of a human (or other animal) is <u>affected by upbringing</u> in some way, however small. In fact it's considerably <u>easier</u> to list the factors which <u>aren't</u> affected in any way by environment.

> **Characteristics not affected at all by environment:**
>
> 1) <u>Eye colour</u>
> 2) <u>Hair colour</u> in most animals (in humans, vanity plays a big part)
> 3) <u>Inherited diseases</u> like haemophilia, cystic fibrosis, etc.
> 4) <u>Blood group</u>
>
>   Learn these four in case they ask you about them.

<u>Environment</u> can have a large effect on
characteristics even <u>before</u> someone's born.
A baby's <u>weight</u> at birth can be affected by things like
the mother's <u>diet</u> and whether or not she <u>smokes</u>.

I bet you could do with some variation right now...

The big thing to remember here is that variation is about comparing animals or plants of the <u>same species</u>, not just any random ones. <u>Cover the page</u> and <u>scribble down</u> the details.

Genes and Variation

DNA and Mutation

DNA — deoxy... something or other. It's quite important apparently.

DNA — a Double Helix of Paired Bases

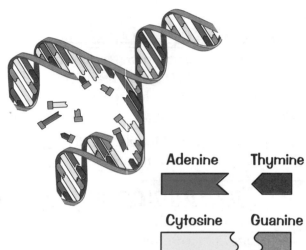

1) A DNA molecule is two strands coiled together in the shape of a <u>double helix</u>, as shown in the diagram opposite. Very fancy.

2) The DNA double helix is made up of <u>four</u> different "<u>bases</u>" (shown in the diagram as different colours).

3) The bases are <u>paired</u>, and they <u>always</u> pair up in the same way — Adenine goes with Thymine, Cytosine goes with Guanine. This pairing is essential in enabling DNA to <u>replicate itself</u>. As the two strands unwind, bases floating around them inside the cell nucleus join on where they fit — giving two <u>identical</u> DNA molecules. That's what's happening in the diagram.

Adenine   Thymine

Cytosine   Guanine

Learn these four names.

Radiation and Certain Chemicals cause Mutations

A <u>mutation</u> is a <u>change</u> in the <u>chemical structure</u> of a gene — a fault in the DNA. <u>Mutations occur 'naturally'</u>, probably caused by "natural" background radiation (from the Sun, and rocks etc.) or just the laws of chance that every now and then the DNA doesn't quite <u>copy itself</u> properly.

However <u>the chance of mutation is increased</u> by exposing yourself to:

1) <u>IONISING RADIATION</u>, including <u>X-rays</u> and <u>Ultra-Violet light</u>, (which are the highest-frequency parts of the <u>EM spectrum</u>) together with radiation from <u>radioactive substances</u>. For each of these examples, the <u>greater</u> the <u>dose</u> of radiation, the <u>greater</u> the <u>chance</u> of mutation.

2) <u>CERTAIN CHEMICALS</u> which are known to cause mutations. Such chemicals are called <u>mutagens</u>. If the mutations produce cancer then the chemicals are often called <u>carcinogens</u>. Cigarette smoke contains chemical mutagens (or carcinogens). Nice.

The Human Genome Project is a Catalogue of our Genes

<u>Genome</u> is one of those fancy Biology words. It means all the genes that a plant or animal has.

1) The <u>Human Genome Project</u> is a complete <u>catalogue</u> of the <u>DNA</u> of every single gene in every chromosome in the human body.

2) In the future, the Human Genome Project may make it possible to <u>screen</u> for <u>genetic diseases</u>, or for genes that make things like heart disease or cancer more likely.

3) There are potential problems though. If <u>genetic information</u> is available to <u>insurance companies</u>, people with <u>genes</u> that make them more likely to suffer from <u>heart disease</u> or <u>cancer</u> might find it very <u>hard</u> to get life insurance. They might ask you about this sort of thing in the Exam.

Don't get all knotted up with yourself, relax and enjoy...

Three headings on this page. Memorise the <u>headings first</u>, then learn the <u>numbered points</u>. Cover the page and <u>scribble down</u> everything you can remember. <u>Keep doing it</u> until you've <u>got it all</u>.

Monohybrid Crosses

Genes and Variation

"Hey man, like *monohybrid crosses*, yeah right...   ...so like, *what does it mean*, man?"   Just this, pal:

Breeding <u>two plants</u> or <u>animals</u>, who have <u>one gene different</u>, to see what you <u>get</u>.

It's always best done with a diagram like either of these:

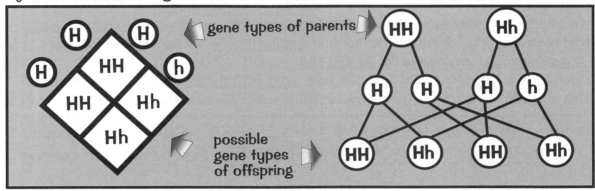

But first learn all these technical terms — it's real difficult to follow what's going on if you don't:

1) ALLELE

— this is just another name for a <u>GENE</u>. If you have <u>two different versions of a gene</u>, like H and h, then you have to call them <u>ALLELES</u> instead of genes. Defective/altered alleles can cause inherited disease.

2) DOMINANT AND RECESSIVE

— self explanatory. A dominant allele <u>DOMINATES</u> a recessive allele.

3) GENOTYPE AND PHENOTYPE

— <u>GENOTYPE</u> is just what '<u>type o' genes</u>' you've got, eg. HH, Hh, or hh.
PHENOTYPE sounds a lot like genotype but, irritatingly, is nothing like it at all.
Genotype is always a pair of letters like Hh, whilst <u>PHENOTYPE</u> is what <u>physical characteristics</u> result from the genotype, like "blue hair" or "big leaves" or "maleness".

4) "PARENTAL", "F1" AND "F2" GENERATIONS

— pretty obvious. The two <u>originals</u> that you cross are the <u>parental generation</u>, their <u>kids</u> are the <u>F1 generation</u> and the "<u>grandchildren</u>" are the <u>F2 generation</u>. Easy peasy.

5) HOMOZYGOUS AND HETEROZYGOUS

— "Homo-" means "same kinda things", "Hetero-" means "different kinda things".
They stick "<u>-zygous</u>" on the end to show we're talking about <u>genes</u>, (rather than any other aspect of Biology), and also just to make it <u>sound more complicated</u>, I'm certain of it. So...

"<u>HOMOZYGOUS RECESSIVE</u>" is the descriptive shorthand (hah!) for this:	hh
"<u>HOMOZYGOUS DOMINANT</u>" is the 'shorthand' for	HH
"<u>HETEROZYGOUS</u>" is the 'shorthand' for	Hh
"<u>A HOMOZYGOTE</u>" or "<u>A HETEROZYGOTE</u>" are how you refer to people with such genes.	

Let's try out the brilliant descriptive "shorthand" shall we:
"Alexander is homozygous recessive for the baldness gene" is <u>so much easier</u> to say and understand than "Alex is bb". Hmm, well, that's Biology for you...

Homozygote trousers — a pair of genes...

You can't beat a fewdal big fancyfold wordsmiths to make things crystally clearasil, can you...
Anyway, half the Exam marks are for knowing the fancy words <u>so just keep learning 'em!</u>

Higher

Genes and Variation

Monohybrid Crosses: Hamsters

Cross-breeding Hamsters

It can be all too easy to find yourself cross-breeding hamsters, some with normal hair and a mild disposition and others with wild scratty hair and a leaning towards crazy acrobatics.

Let's say that the gene which causes the crazy nature is <u>recessive</u>, so we use a <u>small "h"</u> for it, whilst normal (boring) behaviour is due to a <u>dominant gene</u>, so we represent it with a <u>capital "H"</u>.

1) A <u>crazy hamster</u> must have the <u>GENOTYPE</u>:   hh.

2) However, a <u>NORMAL HAMSTER</u> can have <u>TWO POSSIBLE GENOTYPES</u>:   HH or Hh.

This is pretty important — it's the basic difference between dominant and recessive genes:

> To display <u>RECESSIVE CHARACTERISTICS</u> you must have
> <u>BOTH ALLELES RECESSIVE</u>, hh, (ie. be "homozygous recessive")
>
> But to display <u>DOMINANT CHARACTERISTICS</u> you can be
> <u>EITHER</u> HH ("homozygous dominant") or Hh ("heterozygous").

It's only that difference which makes monohybrid crosses even <u>remotely</u> interesting.   If hh gave crazy hamsters, HH gave normal hamsters and Hh something in between, it'd all be pretty dull.

An Almost Unbearably Exciting Example

Let's take a <u>thoroughbred crazy hamster</u>, genotype hh, with a <u>thoroughbred normal hamster</u>, genotype HH, and cross-breed them.   You must learn this whole diagram thoroughly, till you can do it all yourself:

P1 Parents' <u>PHENOTYPE</u>:   <u>Normal and boring</u>   <u>Wild and scratty</u>

P1 Parents' <u>GENOTYPE</u>:   (HH)   (hh)

Gametes' <u>GENOTYPE</u>:   (H)   (H)   (h)   (h)

F1 Zygotes' <u>GENOTYPE</u>:   (Hh)   (Hh)   (Hh)   (Hh)

F1 Zygotes' <u>PHENOTYPE</u>:   <u>They're all normal and boring</u>

<u>If two of these F1 generation now breed they will produce the F2 generation</u>:

F1 Parents' <u>PHENOTYPE</u>:   <u>Normal and boring</u>   <u>Normal and boring</u>

F1 Parents' <u>GENOTYPE</u>:   (Hh)   (Hh)

Gametes' <u>GENOTYPE</u>:   (H)   (h)   (H)   (h)

F2 Zygotes' <u>GENOTYPE</u>:   (HH)   (Hh)   (hH)   (hh)

F2 Zygotes' *PHENOTYPE*:   Normal   Normal   Normal   *CRAZY!*

This gives a <u>3 : 1 RATIO</u> of Normal to Crazy offspring in the F2 generation.
Remember that "<u>results</u>" like this are only <u>PROBABILITIES</u>.   It doesn't mean it'll happen.
(Most likely, you'll end up trying to contain a mini-riot of nine lunatic baby hamsters.)

See how those fancy words start to roll off the tongue...

The diagram and all its fancy words need to be second nature to you.   So practise writing it out <u>from memory</u> until you get it all right.   Because when you can do one — <u>you can do 'em all</u>.

Genetic Engineering

Genetically Modified Organisms

Genetic engineering is a new science with exciting possibilities, but dangers, too.

Genetic Engineering *is* Ace — *hopefully*

The basic idea of genetic engineering is to move sections of <u>DNA</u> (genes) from one organism to another so that it produces <u>useful biological products</u>.

1) Crops such as <u>wheat</u> are <u>genetically modified</u> to be <u>resistant to weedkillers</u>. The farmer can spray the <u>whole field</u> with weedkiller and <u>only kill</u> the <u>weeds</u>.

2) Other food crops are genetically modified to be better for consumers. <u>Tomatoes</u> are genetically modified so that they <u>ripen more slowly</u>. This makes them <u>taste better</u> and go off less quickly.

3) Bacteria are used to produce <u>human insulin</u> for diabetes sufferers and also to produce <u>human growth hormone</u> for children who aren't growing properly.

Genetic Engineering *involves these Important Stages:*

1) The useful gene is "<u>cut</u>" from the DNA of, say, a human.
2) This is done using <u>enzymes</u>. Particular enzymes will cut out particular bits of DNA.
3) <u>Enzymes</u> are then used to <u>cut the DNA</u> of a <u>bacterium</u> and the human gene is then inserted.
4) Again this "<u>splicing</u>" of a new gene is controlled by certain <u>specific enzymes</u>.
5) The bacterium is now <u>cultivated</u> and soon there are <u>millions</u> of similar bacteria all producing, say, human insulin.
6) This can be done on an <u>industrial scale</u> and the useful product can be <u>separated out</u>.
7) The same approach can also be used to <u>transfer useful genes into animal embryos</u>. Sheep for example can be developed which produce useful substances (ie. drugs) in <u>their milk</u>! This is a very easy way to produce drugs...

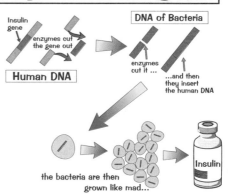

Genetic Engineering — Benefits and Problems

<u>Genetic engineering</u> of <u>crops</u> could make it possible to grow them in places they wouldn't grow before — good news for countries with lousy climates. Crops could also be genetically engineered to be more nutritious — preventing <u>malnutrition</u>.

Engineering weedkiller-resistant crops is a great way of <u>increasing yields</u>, but there are potential problems. Some people worry that farmers should be spraying <u>less</u> weedkiller on the land not more.

Genetic engineering of <u>humans</u> is currently restricted to <u>gene therapy</u> for diseases like cystic fibrosis that are caused by <u>faulty genes</u>. This means introducing <u>healthy</u> copies of the gene into the body of a person with the disease. Their <u>cells</u> will then be able to make the protein they need.

Genetic engineering of <u>sperm</u> and <u>egg</u> cells would allow genetic diseases to be eliminated in <u>future generations</u>. It could also be used to create '<u>designer babies</u>' with only the genetic traits preferred by their parents. A lot of people are strongly <u>against</u> this.

Now I'm ready to create my monster

Genetic engineering — it's a bit like my cat. Except it doesn't pounce on things. And it doesn't eat loads. And you can't stroke it. And it doesn't purr. And it can't miaow. And it doesn't...

Population Sizes

This is all about how many of one type of animal there are in an environment.

The Size of any Population depends on Three Factors

The size of the population of any animal or plant is due to THREE FACTORS:

1) COMPETITION — how well the animal competes with other species (and members of its own species) for the same food.
Plants and animals compete in similar ways:
 a) Plants often compete with each other for space, and for water and nutrients from the soil.
 b) Animals often compete with each other for space, food and water.

2) ADAPTATION — how well the animal has become adapted to its environment.

3) PREDATION — how well the animal avoids being eaten.

It's also going to depend on other things like the amount of food available, and how many of the species die from diseases or migrate to other places. But that's kind of obvious.

Generally organisms will thrive best if:

1) There's plenty of the good things in life: food, water, space, shelter, light, etc.
2) They're better than the competition at getting it (better adapted).
3) They don't get eaten.
4) They don't get ill.

That's pretty much the long and short of it. Learn those four things, because they're the basic principles that will always apply in an Exam question about population.

Populations of Prey and Predators go in Cycles

In a community containing prey and predators (as most of them do of course):

1) The population of any species is usually limited by the amount of food available.
2) If the population of the prey increases, then so will the population of the predators.
3) However as the population of predators increases, the number of prey will decrease.

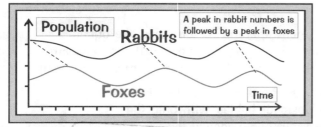

ie. More grass means more rabbits.
More rabbits means more foxes.
But more foxes means fewer rabbits.
Eventually fewer rabbits will mean fewer foxes again.
This up and down pattern continues...

Revision stress — don't let it eat you up...

It's a strange topic is population sizes. In a way it seems like common sense, but it all seems to get so messy. Anyway, learn all the points on this page and you'll have no problem, I'd think. And remember — you can forget it all once the exam's over and done

Adapt and Survive

If you <u>learn the features</u> that make these animals well adapted, you'll be able to apply them to any other similar animal they might give you in the Exam. Chances are you'll get a <u>camel</u> or a <u>polar bear</u> anyway.

The Polar Bear and Camel are Adapted for Different Conditions

The <u>Polar bear</u> has all these features:

1) <u>Large rounded shape</u> including dinky little ears, to keep the <u>surface area</u> to a minimum (compared to the body weight) — this <u>reduces heat loss</u>.
2) A thick layer of <u>blubber</u> for <u>insulation</u>.
3) <u>Thick hairy coat</u> for keeping the body heat in.
4) <u>Greasy fur</u> which sheds water after swimming.
5) <u>White fur</u> to match the surroundings for <u>camouflage</u>.
6) <u>Big feet</u> to <u>spread the weight</u> on snow and ice.

The <u>camel</u> has all these features: (most of which are shared by <u>other desert creatures</u>...)

1) It can <u>store</u> a lot of <u>water</u> without problem.
2) It loses very little water.
   There's little <u>urine</u> and very little <u>sweating</u>.
3) It can tolerate <u>big changes</u> in its own <u>body temperature</u> to remove the need for sweating.
4) <u>Large feet</u> to <u>spread load</u> on soft sand.

The Fish — Designed for Water Conditions

1) <u>Gills</u> to allow it to <u>breathe under water</u>.
2) A <u>streamlined</u> shape and <u>fins</u> for <u>speed</u> underwater.
3) <u>Light-coloured underside</u> and <u>dark-coloured upper body</u> for camouflage.
4) <u>Mucus-covered scales</u> help to <u>protect against infection</u> and to <u>increase swimming speed</u>.

The Cactus is Well Adapted for the Desert

1) It has <u>no leaves</u> — to <u>reduce water loss</u>.
2) It has a <u>small surface area</u> compared to its size, which also <u>reduces water loss</u>. *(1000 x less than normal plants)*
3) It <u>stores water</u> in its thick stem.
4) <u>Spines</u> stop herbivores <u>eating</u> them.
5) <u>Shallow</u> but very extensive roots cover a large area and absorb water quickly to make the most of scarce rainfall.

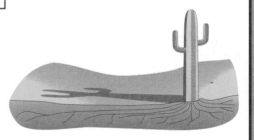

The Rabbit is Adapted to Survive being Prey

1) <u>Fast</u> and <u>agile</u> for escaping capture.
2) <u>Eyes</u> on <u>sides</u> for <u>all-round vision</u>.
3) <u>Big ears</u> for good hearing.
4) Brown colour for <u>camouflage</u>.
5) <u>White tail</u> to alert pals.

Creature features — Adapt and Survive...

It's well worth learning these survival features well enough to be able to write them down <u>from memory</u>. Then you'll be able to apply them to any other animal they might give you in the <u>Exam</u>.

Natural and Artificial Selection

Darwin's Theory of Natural Selection is Ace

THIS THEORY IS COOL and provides a comprehensive explanation for all life on Earth.
Mind you, it caused some trouble at the time, because for the first time ever there was a highly plausible explanation for our own existence, without the need for a "Creator". This was bad news for the religious authorities of the time, who tried to ridicule old Charlie's ideas.
But, as they say, "THE TRUTH WILL OUT".

Darwin made Four Important Observations...

1) All organisms produce MORE OFFSPRING than could possibly survive.
2) But in fact, population numbers tend to remain FAIRLY CONSTANT over long periods of time.
3) Organisms in a species show WIDE VARIATION due to different genes.
4) SOME of the variations are INHERITED AND PASSED ON to the next generation.

...and then made these Two Deductions:

1) Since most offspring don't survive, all organisms must have to STRUGGLE FOR SURVIVAL.
2) The ones who SURVIVE AND REPRODUCE will PASS ON THEIR GENES.

This is the famous "SURVIVAL OF THE FITTEST" statement. Organisms with slightly less survival-value will probably perish first, leaving the strongest and fittest to pass on their genes to the next generation.

Selective Breeding is Very Simple

Selective breeding is also called artificial selection, because humans artificially select the plants or animals that are going to breed and flourish, according to what we want from them.
This is the basic process involved in selective breeding:

1) From your existing stock select the ones which have the best characteristics.
2) Breed them with each other.
3) Select the best of the offspring, and combine them with the best that you already have and breed again.
4) Continue this process over several generations to develop the desired traits.

Selective Breeding is Very Useful in Farming

Artificial selection like this is used in most areas of modern farming, to great benefit:

1) More SHEEP

Selectively breeding sheep to get an increase in the size and number of offspring, and the amount of wool.

2) Better MILK

Selectively breeding milking cows to increase milk yield and resistance to disease.

3) Better WHEAT

Selectively breeding wheat to produce new varieties with better yields and better disease-resistance too.

Survival of the fittest — better go to the gym then...

This stuff isn't much like genetic engineering — farmers have been selectively breeding for ages. Learn all the numbered points because they're flippin' important. Honestly.

Evolution

Selection, Survival and Evolution

The Theory of Evolution is Cool

1) This suggests that all the animals and plants on Earth gradually "evolved" over millions of years, rather than just suddenly popping into existence. Makes sense.

2) Life on Earth began as simple organisms living in water and gradually everything else evolved from there.
And it only took about 3,000,000,000 years.

Fossils Provide Evidence for it

1) Fossils provide lots of evidence for evolution.
2) They show how today's species have changed and developed over millions of years.
3) There are quite a few "missing links" though because the fossil record is incomplete.
4) This is because very very few dead plants or animals actually turn into fossils.
5) Most just decay away completely.

Forefeet

Evolution of the horse

Hyracotherium

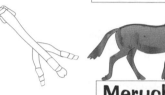
Mesohippus

The Evolution of The Horse is Ace

1) One set of fossils which is pretty good though is that showing the evolution of the horse.
2) This developed from quite a small creature about the size of a dog and the fossils show how the middle toe slowly became bigger and bigger and eventually evolved into the familiar hoof of today's horse.
3) It took about 60 million years though.
4) This is pretty strong evidence in support of evolution because it really shows evolution happening!

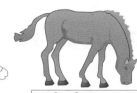
Merychippus

Pliohippus

Modern

Extinction is Pretty Bad News

The dinosaurs and hairy mammoths became extinct and it's only fossils that tell us they ever existed at all, (notwithstanding the odd questionable glacier story).

There are three ways a species can become extinct:
1) The environment changes too quickly.
2) A new predator or disease kills them all.
3) They can't compete with another (new) species for food.

As the environment slowly changes, it will gradually favour certain new characteristics amongst the members of the species and over many generations those features will proliferate. In this way, the species constantly adapts to its changing environment. But if the environment changes too fast the whole species may be wiped out, ie. extinction...

Stop horsing around and just learn the facts...

Another stupefyingly easy page to learn. Use the mini-essay method. Just make sure you learn every fact, that's all. Dinosaurs never did proper revision and look what happened to them.
(Mind you they did last about 200 million years, which is about 199.9 million more than we have, so far...)

Module Two — Inheritance and Survival   EDEXCEL MODULAR SYLLABUS

There Are Too Many People

There's one born every minute — and it's too many

1) The population of the world is currently rising out of control, as the graph shows.

2) This is mostly due to modern medicine, which has stopped widespread death from disease.

3) It's also due to modern farming methods, which can now provide the food needed for so many hungry mouths.

4) The death rate is now much lower than the birth rate in many under-developed countries.

   In other words there are lots more babies born than people dying.

5) This creates big problems for those countries trying to cope with all those extra people.

6) Even providing basic health care and education (about contraception!) is difficult, never mind finding them places to live, and food to eat.

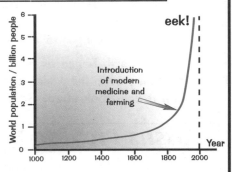

Increasing Living Standards Adds Even More Pressure

The rapidly increasing population is not the only problem. The increasing standard of living amongst more developed countries also demands more from the environment.

These two factors mean that:

1) Raw materials, including non-renewable energy resources (like coal and oil) are being rapidly used up.
2) More and more waste is being produced.
3) Unless waste is properly handled more pollution will be caused.

When the Earth's population was much smaller, the effects of human activity were usually small and local.

More People Means Less Land for Plants and Animals

There are four main ways that humans reduce the amount of land available for other animals and plants.

1) Building

2) Farming

3) Dumping Waste

4) Quarrying

More People Means More Environmental Damage

Human activity can pollute all three parts of the environment:

1) Water – with sewage, fertiliser and toxic chemicals.
2) Air – with smoke and gases such as sulphur dioxide.
3) Land – with toxic chemicals, such as pesticides and herbicides. These may then be washed from the land into water.

Learn the facts first — then you can build your rocket...

It's real scary innit — the way that graph of world population seems to be pointing nearly vertically upwards... tricky. Anyway, you just worry about your Exams instead, and make sure you learn all the grim facts. Four sections — mini-essays for each, till you know it all.

Pollution and Acid Rain

Modern industrial life causes all kinds of pollution. People are usually fine at remembering the sources of pollution, but not so hot on sorting out their effects.

Burning Fossil Fuels Releases CO_2 and Smoke

1) Fossil fuels are coal, oil and natural gas.

2) The main culprits for burning these fuels are cars and power stations.

3) They release mostly carbon dioxide, which adds to the Greenhouse Effect.

4) The smoke that they release also causes pollution — especially when it mixes with fog to make thick brown yucky smog.

Burning Fossil Fuels Causes Acid Rain

1) When fossil fuels are burned they also release other harmful gases:
   a) sulphur dioxide   b) various nitrogen oxides.

2) When these mix with clouds they form acids. This then falls as acid rain.

3) Cars and power stations are the main causes of acid rain.

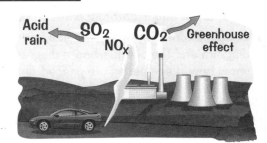

Acid rain ← SO_2 NO_x CO_2 → Greenhouse effect

Acid Rain Kills Fish, Trees and Statues

1) Acid rain causes lakes to become acidic, which has a severe effect on their ecosystems.

2) The acid causes aluminium salts from soil to dissolve into the water. The resulting aluminium ions are poisonous to many fish and birds.

3) Acid rain also kills trees.

4) Acid rain also damages limestone buildings and ruins stone statues.

Car Exhausts produce Lots of Harmful Substances

1) Car exhaust gases contain carbon monoxide, hydrocarbons and nitrogen oxides, among other things.

2) Cars are now being fitted with catalytic converters to clean up their exhaust gases. The nitrogen oxides, hydrocarbons and carbon monoxide are converted to nitrogen and carbon dioxide. Water vapour is also produced.

3) The other way of reducing acid rain is simply to use fewer vehicles. Mind you — taking the bus or train rather than the car is fine in cities, but easier said than done in the countryside.

Revision and Pollution — the two bugbears of modern life...

Don't forget they won't ask you easy stuff like "Is acid rain caused by cars or monkeys?", they'll test you on trickier stuff like "Which gases cause acid rain and why?". Learn it good.

Revision Summary for Module Two

If you can get these puzzlers licked, you should have no problems in the Exam. Use these questions to find out what you know — and what you don't. Then look back and learn the bits you didn't get first time. Then try the questions again, and again...

1) Draw a set of diagrams showing the relationship between: cell, nucleus, chromosomes, genes, DNA.
2) Give a definition of mitosis. Draw a set of diagrams showing what happens in mitosis.
3) What is asexual reproduction? Give a proper definition for it. How does it involve mitosis?
4) Where does meiosis take place? What kind of cells does meiosis produce?
5) Draw out the sequence of diagrams showing what happens during meiosis.
6) What happens to the chromosome numbers during meiosis and then during fertilisation?
7) What is sexual reproduction? Give a proper definition for it.
8) How many pairs of chromosomes are there in a normal human cell nucleus?
9) What are X and Y chromosomes to do with? Who has what combination?
10) Copy and complete the genetic inheritance diagram and the chequerboard diagram to show how these genes are passed on.

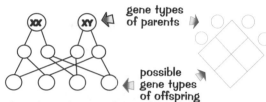

11) Describe the four main characteristics of males and females that change during puberty.
12) Describe the ways in which oestrogen and progesterone control the menstrual cycle.
13) Explain the differences between genetic and environmental variation.
14) Give four characteristics of animals that are not affected at all by environment.
15) What are the names of the four "bases"? How do they make DNA replication work so well?
16) What is a mutation?
17) Name two things that increase the chance of a mutation occurring.
18) Give brief explanations of the following words: a) Allele; b) Homozygous; c) Heterozygous.
19) Give definitions of the following words: a) Genotype; b) Phenotype.
20) What are the fancy terms given to the following combinations of genes: a) HH; b) hh; c) Hh.
21) Starting with parental gene types HH and hh, draw a full genetic inheritance diagram to show the eventual gene types and physical types of the F1 and F2 generations (of hamsters).
22) Give a brief outline of the main stages involved in genetic engineering.
23) Describe the drawbacks and ethical problems concerning the use of genetic engineering.
24) What things can determine the size of a population of a species?
25) Sketch a graph of prey and predator populations and explain the shapes.
26) List six survival features of a polar bear and four survival features of a camel.
27) Describe how a cactus is adapted to living in arid conditions.
28) What were Darwin's four observations and two deductions about natural selection?
29) What is meant by selective breeding? Describe the basic procedure.
30) Explain how fossils found in rocks support the theory of evolution, using the horse as an example.
31) Describe three ways that a species can become extinct.
32) Describe two consequences of increasing population and living standards in the world.
33) Name four ways that humans reduce the amount of land available for other animals and plants.
34) What causes the Greenhouse effect?
35) Name three effects of acid rain.

Atoms

The structure of atoms is dead simple. I mean, gee, there's nothing to them. Just learn and enjoy.

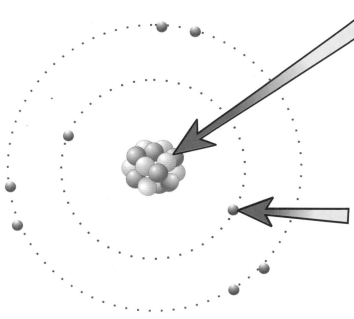

The Nucleus

1) It's in the <u>middle</u> of the atom.
2) It contains <u>protons</u> and <u>neutrons</u>.
3) It has a <u>positive charge</u> because of the protons.
4) Almost the <u>whole mass</u> of the atom is <u>concentrated</u> in the <u>nucleus</u>.
5) But size-wise it's <u>tiny</u> compared to the atom as a whole.

The Electrons

1) Move <u>around</u> the nucleus.
2) They're <u>negatively charged</u>.
3) They're <u>tiny</u>, but they cover a <u>lot of space</u>.
4) The <u>volume</u> of their orbits determines <u>how big</u> the atom is.
5) They have <u>virtually no mass</u>.
6) They occupy <u>shells</u> around the nucleus.
7) These shells explain the <u>whole of Chemistry</u>.

Atoms are <u>dead tiny</u>, don't forget. They're <u>too small to see</u>, even with a microscope.

1) Neutral atoms have <u>no charge</u> overall.
2) The <u>charge</u> on the <u>electrons</u> is the <u>same size</u> as the charge on the <u>protons</u> but <u>opposite</u>.
3) This means the <u>number of protons</u> always <u>equals</u> the <u>number of electrons</u> in a <u>neutral atom</u>.
4) The number of neutrons isn't fixed but is usually <u>just a bit higher</u> than the number of protons.
5) The number of protons in an atom is called the <u>ATOMIC NUMBER</u>.
6) The number of neutrons and the number of protons added together is called the <u>MASS NUMBER</u>.

Electrons Are Arranged in *Shells*

1) Electrons are arranged in '<u>shells</u>' around the nucleus.
2) Shells closer to the nucleus are <u>always filled first</u>.
3) Only <u>a certain number</u> of electrons are allowed in each shell:
   <u>1st shell</u>: **2**   <u>2nd Shell</u>: **8**   <u>3rd Shell</u>: **8**
4) Atoms are much <u>happier</u> when they have <u>full electron shells</u>.
5) In most atoms the <u>outer shell</u> is <u>not full</u> and this makes the atom want to <u>react</u>.

It's all different for shells after the 20th element, but you don't need those for now.

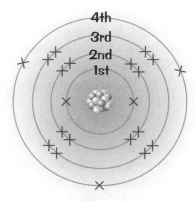

4th shell still filling

Basic atom facts — they don't take up much space...

This stuff on atoms should be permanently engraved in the minds of everyone.
I don't understand how people can get through the day without knowing this stuff, really I don't.
<u>Learn it now</u>, and watch as the Universe unfolds and reveals its timeless mysteries to you...

Elements and
The Periodic Table

The Periodic Table

Something containing only one kind of atom is called an element. As there are only about 100 different kinds of atom, there's only this number of elements. Simple really.

The Modern Periodic Table is Ace

The Periodic Table shows all the elements arranged in a dead useful way. It's lovely. You'll see. And important too, since these elements are the 'building blocks' of everything.

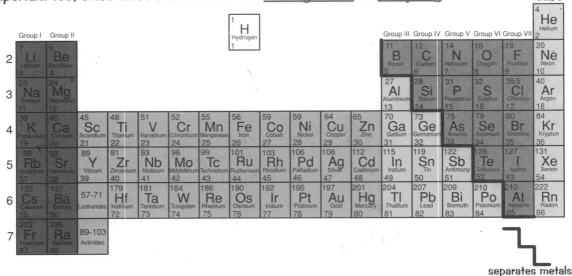

separates metals
from non-metals

1) The Periodic Table shows the elements in order of atomic number.
2) It's laid out so that elements with similar properties are in columns.
3) These vertical columns are called Groups and Roman Numerals are often used for them.
4) For example the Group I elements are Li, Na, K, Rb (plus a couple of others).
   They're all metals which have many similar properties.
5) The rows are called periods. Each new period represents another full shell of electrons.
6) The elements in each Group all have the same number of electrons in their outer shell.
7) That's why they have similar properties. And that's why we arrange them in this way.

More than Three–Quarters of the Elements are Metals

As well as knowing where the boundary between metals and non-metals is, you need to know where these three Groups of elements are.

1) The Alkali metals,
2) The Halogens,
3) The Noble gases.

The elements in each Group have similar properties — although these properties change gradually as you go down the Group.

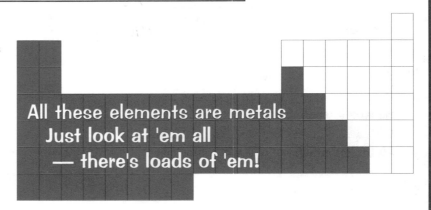

All these elements are metals
Just look at 'em all
— there's loads of 'em!

Periodic table — it's all elementary... *(By the way, I'll be using this pun again)*

Three quarters of all elements are metals — so it stands to reason that they'll be in the Exam. Make sure you know which side of the table the metals are on. You're going to get very familiar with the Periodic Table — learn to love it — let it be your friend. Mmm, lovely.

Electron Arrangements

Elements and The Periodic Table

Nobody expects you to learn the whole periodic table, but you need to know how it's formed.

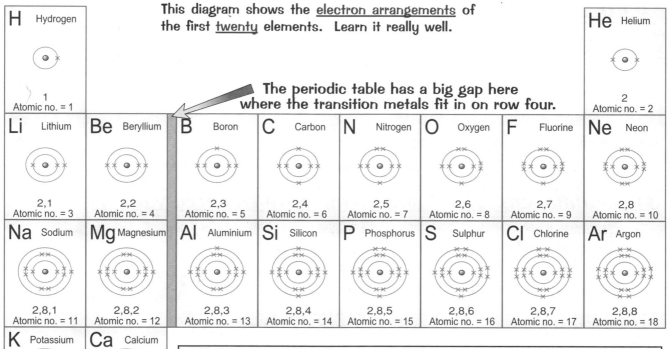

This diagram shows the <u>electron arrangements</u> of the first <u>twenty</u> elements. Learn it really well.

The periodic table has a big gap here where the transition metals fit in on row four.

H Hydrogen							He Helium
1 Atomic no. = 1							2 Atomic no. = 2

Li Lithium	Be Beryllium	B Boron	C Carbon	N Nitrogen	O Oxygen	F Fluorine	Ne Neon
2,1 Atomic no. = 3	2,2 Atomic no. = 4	2,3 Atomic no. = 5	2,4 Atomic no. = 6	2,5 Atomic no. = 7	2,6 Atomic no. = 8	2,7 Atomic no. = 9	2,8 Atomic no. = 10

Na Sodium	Mg Magnesium	Al Aluminium	Si Silicon	P Phosphorus	S Sulphur	Cl Chlorine	Ar Argon
2,8,1 Atomic no. = 11	2,8,2 Atomic no. = 12	2,8,3 Atomic no. = 13	2,8,4 Atomic no. = 14	2,8,5 Atomic no. = 15	2,8,6 Atomic no. = 16	2,8,7 Atomic no. = 17	2,8,8 Atomic no. = 18

K Potassium	Ca Calcium
2,8,8,1 Atomic no. = 19	2,8,8,2 Atomic no. = 20

Reactivity Changes <u>down the Groups due to</u> <u>Shielding</u>

1) As atoms get <u>bigger</u>, they have more <u>full shells</u> of electrons.

2) As you go down any Group, each <u>new row</u> has <u>one more</u> full shell.

3) The number of <u>outer</u> electrons is the <u>same</u> for each element in a Group.

4) However the outer shell of electrons is <u>increasingly far</u> from the nucleus.

5) You have to learn to say that the inner shells provide '<u>shielding</u>'.

6) This means that the <u>outer shell</u> electrons get <u>shielded</u> from the <u>attraction</u> of the <u>+ve nucleus</u>.   The upshot of all this is:

As Metal Atoms <u>get Bigger, the Outer</u> Electron <u>is More Easily Lost</u>

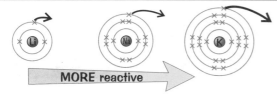

MORE reactive

This makes ***METALS MORE REACTIVE*** as you go ***DOWN*** Group I and Group II.

As <u>Non-metal Atoms get Bigger, the Extra Electrons are Harder to Gain</u>

This makes ***NON-METALS LESS REACTIVE*** as you go ***DOWN*** Group VI and Group VII.

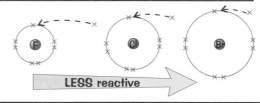

LESS reactive

Learn about Electron Shielding — and keep up with the trends...

It's pretty important that you understand that the arrangement of electrons in an atom isn't just about Feng Shui — it makes a real difference to the <u>reactivity</u> of the atom. Make sure you know the stuff on this page inside out. And you know what I'm going to say — write it all out, <u>mini-essay</u> style.

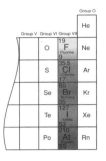

The Properties of Halogens

Group VII — The Halogens

There are four halogens you need to know about: <u>Fluorine</u>, <u>Chlorine</u>, <u>Bromine</u> and <u>Iodine</u>.

Learn These Trends:

As you go <u>*DOWN*</u> Group VII, the <u>*HALOGENS*</u> have the following properties:

1) **Less Reactive**
2) **Higher melting point**
3) **Higher boiling point**

Learn the <u>states</u> of the halogens at <u>room temperature</u>:

| Fluorine: Gas | Chlorine: Gas | Bromine: Liquid | Iodine: Solid |

1) **The Halogens are all <u>non-metals</u> with <u>coloured vapours</u>**

<u>Fluorine</u> is a very reactive, poisonous, <u>yellow gas</u>.

<u>Chlorine</u> is a fairly reactive, poisonous, <u>dense green gas</u>.

<u>Bromine</u> is a dense, poisonous, <u>red-brown volatile liquid</u>.

<u>Iodine</u> is a <u>dark grey</u> crystalline <u>solid</u> or a <u>purple vapour</u>.

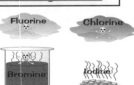

2) **The Halogens react with <u>metals</u> to form <u>salts</u>**

They react with most metals including <u>iron</u> and <u>aluminium</u>, to form <u>salts</u> (or '<u>metal halides</u>').

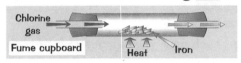

The examiners will expect you to be able to <u>balance chemical equations</u> in the Module 3 test. See pages 50 and 51 for more info about this.

$$2Na_{(s)} + Cl_{2\,(g)} \rightarrow 2NaCl_{(s)}$$
(Sodium chloride)

$$2Fe_{(s)} + 3Br_{2\,(g)} \rightarrow 2FeBr_{3\,(s)}$$
(Iron(III) bromide)

3) **More reactive Halogens will <u>displace</u> less reactive ones**

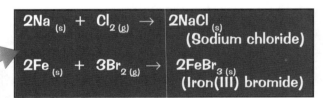

Cl_2 gas

Solution of Potassium iodide

Iodine forming in solution

<u>Chlorine</u> can displace <u>bromine</u> and <u>iodine</u> from a solution of <u>bromide</u> or <u>iodide</u>. <u>Bromine</u> will also displace <u>iodine</u> because of the <u>trend</u> in <u>reactivity</u>.

$$Cl_{2\,(g)} + 2KI_{(aq)} \rightarrow I_{2\,(aq)} + 2KCl_{(aq)}$$

$$Cl_{2\,(g)} + 2KBr_{(aq)} \rightarrow Br_{2\,(aq)} + 2KCl_{(aq)}$$

<u>Chlorine</u> is used in <u>bleach</u> and for <u>sterilising water</u>

1) <u>Chlorine</u> dissolved in <u>sodium hydroxide</u> solution is called <u>bleach</u>.

2) <u>Chlorine compounds</u> are also used to <u>kill germs</u> in swimming pools and drinking water.

<u>Iodine</u> is used as an <u>antiseptic</u>...

...but it stings like nobody's business and stains the skin <u>brown</u>. Nice.

I've never liked Halogens — they give me a bad head...

I think Halogens are as exciting as white-water rafting (ahem). They change colour and go from gases to liquid to solid. What could be more fun than that. Anyway, <u>just learn the facts</u>.

Rates of Reaction

I'll be honest with you... examiners love to test this stuff. It's perfect for asking questions about. It's not difficult, it just takes a little bit of getting used to.

Reactions can go at all sorts of different rates

1) One of the slowest is the rusting of iron (it's not slow enough though — what about my little MGB).

2) Other slow reactions include chemical weathering, like acid rain damage to limestone buildings.

3) A metal (like magnesium) reacting with an acid to produce a gentle stream of bubbles is a moderate speed reaction.

4) A really fast reaction is an explosion, where it's all over in a fraction of a second.

The Rate of a Reaction Depends on Four Things

And you need to know all about them, I'm afraid. They are...

1) TEMPERATURE
2) CONCENTRATION — (or PRESSURE for gases)
3) CATALYST
4) SIZE OF PARTICLES — (or SURFACE AREA)

Three ways to Measure the Speed of a Reaction

The speed of reaction can be observed either by how quickly the reactants are used up or how quickly the products are forming. It's usually a lot easier to measure products forming.

There are three different ways that the speed of a reaction can be measured:

1) Precipitation

This is when the product of the reaction is a precipitate which clouds the solution. Observe a marker through the solution and measure how long it takes for it to disappear.

2) Change in Mass (usually gas given off)

Any reaction that produces a gas can be carried out on a mass balance and as the gas is released the mass disappearing is easily measured.

3) The Volume of gas given off

This involves the use of a gas syringe to measure the volume of gas given off. But that's about all there is to it.

How to get a fast, furious reaction — crack a wee joke...

There's not too much on this page really — but what there is you have to know really well. There are four things that affect the speed of a reaction, and three ways you can measure different reaction rates. Learn these seven facts, and it'll make life so much easier for you.

Collision Theory

Rates of Reaction

Reaction rates are explained perfectly by the collision theory. It's really simple.
It just says that the rate of a reaction simply depends on how often and how hard
the reacting particles collide with each other. The basic idea is that particles
have to collide in order to react, and they have to collide hard enough as well.

More Collisions increases the Rate of Reaction

All the methods of increasing the rate of reactions can be explained in terms of increasing the
number of successful collisions between the reacting particles:

1) TEMPERATURE increases the number of collisions

When the temperature is increased the particles all move quicker.
If they're moving quicker, they're going to have more collisions.

Cold   Hot

2) CONCENTRATION (or PRESSURE) increases the number of collisions

If the solution is made more concentrated it means there are more
particles of reactant knocking about between the water molecules,
which makes collisions between the important particles more likely.
In a gas, increasing the pressure means the molecules are more
squashed up together so there are going to be more collisions.

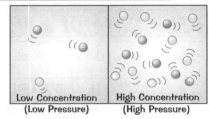
Low Concentration (Low Pressure)   High Concentration (High Pressure)

3) SIZE OF SOLID PARTICLES (or SURFACE AREA) increases collisions

If one of the reactants is a solid then breaking it up into
smaller pieces will increase its surface area. This means
the particles around it in the solution will have more area
to work on so there'll be more useful collisions.

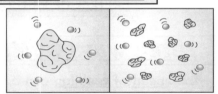

4) CATALYST increases the number of collisions

A catalyst works by giving the reacting particles
a surface to stick to where they can bump into each other.
This increases the number of successful collisions
(by lowering the activation energy) too.

Surface of catalyst

Faster Collisions increase the Rate of Reaction

Higher temperature also increases the energy of the collisions, because it makes all the particles move faster.

Faster collisions are ONLY caused by increasing the temperature

Reactions only happen if the particles collide with enough
energy. At a higher temperature there will be more particles
colliding with enough energy to make the reaction happen.
This initial energy is known as the activation energy, and it's
needed to break the initial bonds.

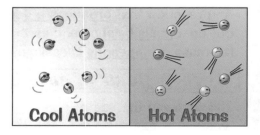
Cool Atoms   Hot Atoms

Collision Theory — I reckon it's always women drivers...

This is quite easy I reckon. It's all pretty obvious — at least once you've been told it, anyway.
The more often particles collide and the harder they hit, the greater the reaction rate. There's a
few extra picky details of course (isn't there always!), but you've only got to LEARN them...

Enzymes

Enzymes seem to crop up in all sorts of places in chemistry. That's because they're great.

Enzymes _are_ Biological Catalysts

1) <u>Living things</u> have thousands of different chemical processes going on inside them.

2) The <u>quicker</u> these happen the <u>better</u>, and raising the <u>temperature</u> of the body is an important way to <u>speed them up</u>.

3) However, there's a <u>limit</u> to how far you can <u>raise</u> the temperature before <u>cells</u> start getting <u>damaged</u>, so living things also produce <u>enzymes</u> which act as <u>catalysts</u> to <u>speed up</u> all these chemical reactions without the need for <u>high temperatures</u>.

Enzymes _are produced by Living Things_ — _and they're Ace_

1) Every <u>different</u> biological process has its <u>own enzyme</u> designed especially for it.

2) Enzymes have <u>two main advantages</u> over <u>non-organic</u> catalysts:
   a) They're <u>not scarce</u> like many metal catalysts eg. platinum.
   b) They work best at <u>low temperatures</u>, which keeps <u>costs down</u>.

Enzymes _Like it Warm but Not Too Hot_

1) The chemical reactions in <u>living cells</u> are quite fast in conditions that are <u>warm</u> rather than <u>hot</u>.

2) This is because the cells use <u>enzyme</u> catalysts, which are <u>protein molecules</u>.

3) Enzymes are usually <u>damaged</u> by temperatures above about <u>45°C</u>, and as the graph shows, their activity drops off <u>sharply</u> when the temperature gets <u>a little too high</u>.

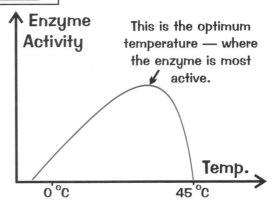

This is the optimum temperature — where the enzyme is most active.

Enzymes _Like the right pH too_

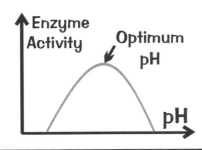

1) The <u>pH</u> affects the activity of enzymes, in a similar way to temperature.

2) The graph shows how the enzyme activity reaches a <u>peak</u> at a certain pH. If the pH is above or below this optimum level, the enzyme activity <u>falls</u>.

3) <u>Different</u> enzymes have <u>different</u> optimum pH levels.

"Enzymes" — sounds like a brand of throat lozenge...

Enzymes are like my cat — they're pretty fussy about just about everything. Not only do they like the temperature to be just right — the pH has to be pretty much spot on as well. This page is definitely a candidate for the mini-essay method. Two mini-essays in fact. What else is there to say? <u>Scribble down the facts, then look back and see what you missed</u>.

Revision Summary for Module Three

These certainly aren't the easiest questions you're going to come across. That's because they test what you know without giving you any clues. At first you might think they're impossibly difficult. Eventually you'll realise that they simply test whether you've learnt the stuff or not. If you're struggling to answer these then you need to go back, take another look at the whole section and then... you guessed it... have another go at the questions.

1) What are the three particles found in an atom?

2) Sketch an atom. Give five details about the nucleus and five details about the electrons.

3) How many electrons does it take to fill: a) the first shell?

                                                       b) the second shell?

                                                       c) the third shell?

4) What's the technical name for rows of the Periodic Table?

5) What feature of atoms determines the order of the modern Periodic Table?

6) Roughly what proportion of the elements are metals?

7) Name the elements shown below:

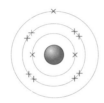 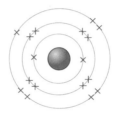

8) Draw diagrams to show the electron arrangements for the first twenty elements.

9) Explain the trend in reactivity of metals and non-metals using the idea of "shielding".

10) Describe the states of the first four halogens at room temperature.

11) Describe the trends in reactivity, boiling points and melting points of the halogens as you go down the Group.

12) List three properties common to all the halogens. Write down two uses of halogens.

13) Give details, with equations, of the reaction of sodium with chlorine. $2Na + Cl_{2(g)} \rightarrow 2NaCl_{(s)}$

14) Describe the reaction of chlorine with potassium iodide. Write the equation. $Cl_2 + p$

15) Which four things can affect the rate of reaction?

16) Give an extra factor which affects the rate of reaction of gases.

17) What are the methods for measuring the rate of reaction?

18) Explain collision theory. I'll even let you use little diagrams in this one.

19) How can particle collisions be made faster?

20) Give two advantages of enzymes over non-biological catalysts.

21) Sketch the graph for enzyme activity vs temperature, indicating the temperatures.

22) If you were being attacked by an enzyme which two ways could you hurt or kill it?

Crude Oil

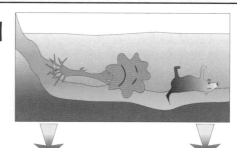

Crude Oil

I'll ease you into this module. It gets harder. Hah hah hah. (That's my evil laugh).

Fossil Fuels _were formed from_ dead plants and animals

1) Fossil fuels have formed over millions of years.

2) Plants and animals died and were immediately covered by sediment in seas or swamps.

3) This stopped them decaying.

4) Further layers of sediment buried the plant and animal remains deeper and deeper.

5) After millions of years of pressure and heat (70°C to 200°C), in an environment with no air, these remains turned into coal, oil and natural gas.

6) When we burn fossil fuels we're using the Sun's energy that has been stored as chemical energy underground for millions of years.

7) Crude oil was originally found as pools of black sludge after it had seeped through to the surface.

8) Once people realised how useful the sludge was they started drilling down for it.

9) Nowadays experts guess where oil might be and then they start drilling.

10) When they strike lucky, the oil is usually under pressure and comes up of its own accord.

1

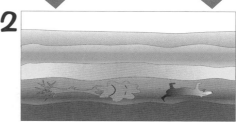

2

Millions of years
of heat and pressure

3

Coal

Crude oil _is a very big part of_ modern life

1) It provides the fuel for most modern transport.

2) It also provides the raw material for making various chemicals including plastics. Plastics are just ace, of course. The world without plastics? Why, it would be the end of civilisation as we know it...

Crude oil **has to be split up to make it useful**

1) Crude oil is a mixture of substances, most of which are different sized hydrocarbon molecules containing carbon and hydrogen only.

2) Hydrocarbons are basically fuels such as petrol and diesel.

3) The bigger and longer the molecules, the less runny the hydrocarbon (fuel) is.

4) Fractional distillation splits crude oil up into its separate fractions.

5) The shorter the molecules, the lower the temperature at which that fraction condenses.

Revising for oil — you know the drill...

There are three sections on this page, with a total of 17 important points. You do realise that they won't ask you what colour oil is or whether it grows on trees or comes out of the ground. No, they'll ask you about these more technical details, so make sure you learn them all. When you think you know it all, cover up the page and scribble down all the details.

Distillation of Crude Oil

Crude Oil

Crude oil isn't a lot of use until it's been fractionally distilled — then its fractions can be used for really important things. The diagram on this page holds the key to this topic, so learn it well.

Crude Oil is Split into Separate Hydrocarbons (fuels)

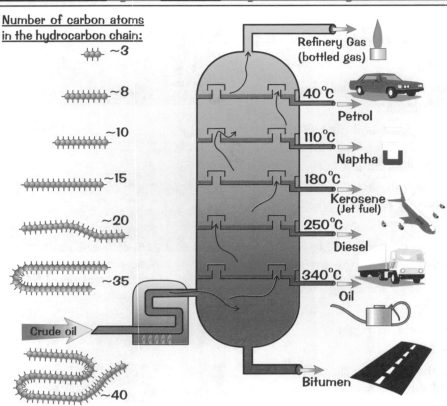

Number of carbon atoms in the hydrocarbon chain:

~3
~8
~10
~15
~20
~35
~40

Crude oil

Refinery Gas (bottled gas)
40°C Petrol
110°C Naptha
180°C Kerosene (Jet fuel)
250°C Diesel
340°C Oil
Bitumen

The <u>fractionating column</u> works continuously, with heated crude oil piped in <u>at the bottom</u> and the various <u>fractions</u> being constantly tapped off at the different levels where they <u>condense</u>.

Hydrocarbons are long chain molecules

As the <u>size</u> of the hydrocarbon molecule <u>increases</u>:

1) The **BOILING POINT** increases

2) It gets **LESS FLAMMABLE**
(doesn't set fire so easy)

3) It gets **MORE VISCOUS**
(doesn't flow so easy)

4) It gets **LESS VOLATILE**
(doesn't evaporate so easily)

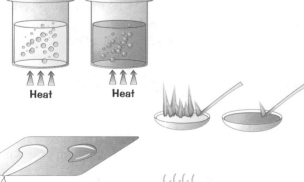

Heat   Heat

The <u>vapours</u> of the more <u>volatile</u> hydrocarbons are <u>very flammable</u> and pose a serious <u>fire risk</u>. So don't smoke at the petrol station. (In fact, don't smoke at all, it's ridiculous.)

Crude oil — just a big ol' mix of stuff...

You need to learn the four features of hydrocarbons which change with increasing chain length. And learn that top diagram because it'll be worth <u>juicy marks</u> in the Exam (and it's pretty too).

Burning Fuels

Ahh... a truly great part of the book. Here you learn about how to build the perfect barbecue with only a twig and a piece of string. Oh, if only chemistry were that interesting.

Burning is Oxidation

When a substance is <u>burnt</u>, <u>oxygen</u> is added to the substance.
This is called <u>oxidation</u>. A good example of oxidation is when methane burns.

methane + oxygen $\longrightarrow$ carbon dioxide + water	(+energy)
CH_4 + $2O_2$ $\longrightarrow$ CO_2 + $2H_2O$	(+energy)

Complete combustion of Hydrocarbons is Safe

1) The <u>complete combustion</u> of any hydrocarbon in oxygen will produce only <u>carbon dioxide</u> and <u>water</u> as waste products.

2) Both are quite <u>clean</u> and <u>non-poisonous</u>.

hydrocarbon + oxygen $\longrightarrow$ carbon dioxide + water   (+ energy)

1) Many <u>gas room heaters</u> release these <u>waste gases</u> into the room, which is perfectly OK.

2) As long as the gas heater is working properly and the room is well ventilated there's no problem.

3) When there's <u>plenty of oxygen</u> the gas burns with a <u>clean blue flame</u>.

But Incomplete combustion of Hydrocarbons is NOT safe

1) If there <u>isn't enough oxygen</u> the combustion will be <u>incomplete</u>.

2) This gives <u>carbon monoxide</u> and <u>carbon</u> as waste products, and produces a <u>smoky yellow flame</u>.

hydrocarbon + oxygen $\longrightarrow$ CO_2 + H_2O + carbon monoxide + carbon   (+ energy)

1) <u>Carbon monoxide</u> is a <u>colourless</u>, <u>odourless</u> and <u>poisonous</u> gas, and it's <u>very dangerous</u>.

2) Every year people are <u>killed</u> while they sleep due to <u>faulty</u> gas fires and boilers filling the room with deadly <u>carbon monoxide</u> (CO) and nobody realising.

3) The black carbon given off produces <u>sooty marks</u> and is a <u>clue</u> that the fuel is <u>not</u> burning fully.

The one burning question is... have you learnt it all...

No barbecue instructions unfortunately, but some things that will help you <u>pass</u> your exams, which is even better. By now this should be engraved on your brain, <u>repeat after me</u>... <u>scribble</u> this all down on a piece of paper and try to <u>remember</u> as much of it as you can until you <u>know it all</u>. You'll be thanking me for this one day, trust me. Right, that's burning fuels over with — may as well go and check out what's next. Looks like we might be on a bit of a roll here.

Alkanes and Alkenes

Crude oil contains both <u>alkanes</u> and <u>alkenes</u>. You need to know the differences between them.

ALKANES have all C–C SINGLE bonds

1) <u>Alkanes</u> are made up of <u>chains</u> of carbon atoms with <u>single</u> covalent bonds between them.
2) They're called <u>saturated</u> hydrocarbons because they have <u>no</u> spare bonds left.
3) This is also why they <u>don't</u> decolourise <u>bromine water</u> — <u>no</u> spare bonds.
4) They <u>won't</u> form polymers — same reason again, <u>no</u> spare bonds.
5) The first four alkanes are <u>methane</u> (natural gas), <u>ethane</u>, <u>propane</u> and <u>butane</u>.
6) They burn cleanly producing <u>carbon dioxide</u> and <u>water</u>.

Bromine water + alkane —still brown.

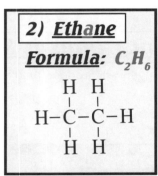

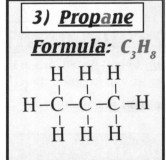

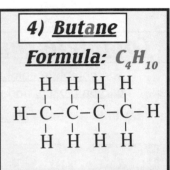

ALKENES have a C=C DOUBLE bond

1) <u>Alkenes</u> are <u>chains</u> of carbon atoms with one <u>double</u> bond.
2) They are called <u>unsaturated</u> hydrocarbons because they have some <u>spare</u> bonds left.
3) This is why they will decolourise <u>bromine water</u>. They form <u>bonds</u> with bromide ions.
4) They form <u>polymers</u> by <u>opening up</u> their double bonds to "<u>hold hands</u>" in a long chain.
5) The first two alkenes are <u>ethene</u> and <u>propene</u>.
6) They tend to burn with a <u>smoky flame</u>, producing <u>soot</u> (carbon).

Bromine water + alkene — decolourised

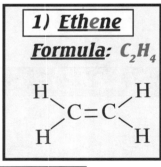

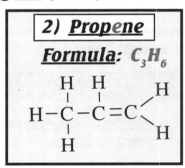

<u>IMPORTANT POINTS</u> to be noted :

1) <u>Bromine water</u> is the <u>standard</u> test to distinguish between alkanes and alkenes.
2) <u>Alkenes</u> are more <u>reactive</u> due to the <u>double</u> bond all poised and ready to just pop open.
3) Notice the names: "<u>Meth-</u>" means "<u>one</u> carbon atom", "<u>eth-</u>" means "<u>two</u> C atoms", "<u>prop-</u>" means "<u>three</u> C atoms", "<u>but-</u>" means "<u>four</u> C atoms", etc. The only difference then between the names of alkanes and alkenes is just the "<u>-ane</u>" or "<u>-ene</u>" on the end.
4) <u>All alkanes</u> have the formula: C_nH_{2n+2} <u>All alkenes</u> have the formula: C_nH_{2n}

Alkane anybody who doesn't learn this lot properly...

All of this is important — but the <u>bromine water</u> test is really important. Learn it well so that if someone comes up to you in the street and asks how to tell an alkane from an alkene, you can quickly and without fuss tell them that an <u>alkene</u> will <u>decolourise bromine water</u>.

Cracking Hydrocarbons

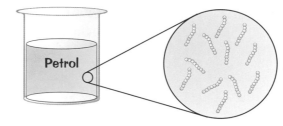

Cracking — splitting up long chain hydrocarbons

1) <u>Long chain</u> hydrocarbons form <u>thick</u> gloopy liquids like <u>tar</u>, which aren't all that useful.
2) The process called <u>cracking</u> turns them into <u>shorter</u> molecules which are <u>much</u> more useful.

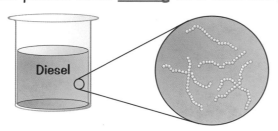

3) <u>Cracking</u> is a form of <u>thermal decomposition</u>, which just means <u>breaking</u> molecules down into <u>simpler</u> molecules by <u>heating</u> them.
4) A lot of the longer molecules produced from fractional distillation are <u>cracked</u> into smaller ones because there's more <u>demand</u> for products like <u>petrol</u> and <u>kerosene</u> (paraffin) than for diesel or lubricating oil.
5) More importantly, cracking produces <u>extra alkenes</u>, which are needed for making <u>plastics</u>.

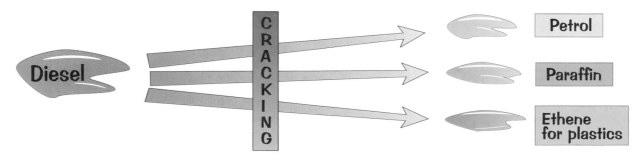

Industrial conditions for cracking: hot, plus a catalyst

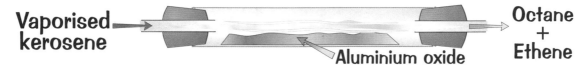

1) <u>Vaporised hydrocarbons</u> are passed over a <u>powdered catalyst</u> at about <u>400°C – 700°C</u>.
2) <u>Aluminium oxide</u> is the catalyst used.
   The <u>long chain</u> molecules <u>split apart</u> or "crack" on the <u>surface</u> of the bits of catalyst.
   This is another of those <u>thermal decomposition</u> reactions.

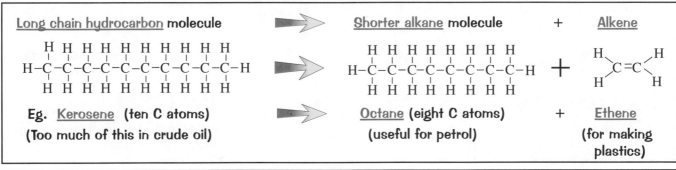

Chemistry — what a cracking subject it is...

Five details about the whys and wherefores, two details of the industrial conditions and a specific example showing typical products: a shorter chain alkane and an alkene. <u>LEARN IT ALL.</u>

Polymers and Plastics

Plastics

Polymers and plastics were first discovered in about 1933. By 1970 it was all too late. Those halcyon days when they made proper motor cars with leather seats and lovely wooden dashboards were over. Sigh.

Alkenes open their double bonds to form Polymers

Under a bit of <u>pressure</u> and with a bit of a <u>catalyst</u> to help it along, many <u>small alkenes</u> will open up their <u>double bonds</u> and "join hands" to form <u>very long chains</u> called <u>polymers</u>. There are three important points you need to know:

1) The process of joining up lots of <u>individual alkenes</u> to form a <u>plastic</u> is called <u>polymerisation</u>.
2) If <u>no other products</u> are formed during the polymerisation reaction, the process is called <u>addition polymerisation</u>.
3) The <u>individual</u> units which "hold hands" to form the polymer are called <u>unsaturated monomers</u>.

<u>Ethene</u> becoming polyethene or "polythene" is the easiest example of polymerisation:

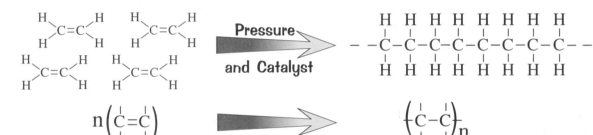

Pressure and Catalyst

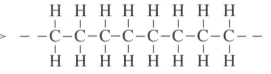

Many single ethenes → Polyethene

There are loads of Plastics with loads of different uses

1) Polythene
1) Made from <u>ethene</u>.
2) Very <u>cheap</u> and <u>strong</u>.
3) Easily <u>moulded</u>.

Bottles, *Plastic bags*, *Bowls*, *Buckets*

2) Polystyrene
1) Made from <u>styrene</u>.
2) <u>Cheap</u> and <u>easily moulded</u>.
3) Can be <u>expanded into foam</u>.

Foam packaging, *Radio outer cases*

3) Polypropene
1) Made from <u>propene</u>.
2) Forms <u>strong fibres</u>.
3) Has <u>high elasticity</u>.

Crates, *Ropes*, *Carpets*

4) Polychloroethene (PVC)
1) Made from <u>chloroethene</u> (also called <u>vinyl chloride</u>).
2) <u>Cheap</u>.
3) Used for making <u>clothes</u> and <u>records</u>.

Records, *Electric wire insulation*

Most plastics don't rot, so they're hard to get rid of

1) Most plastics aren't '<u>biodegradable</u>' — they're not broken down by microorganisms, so they <u>don't rot</u>.
2) It's difficult to get rid of them — if you bury them in a landfill site, they'll <u>still</u> be there <u>years later</u>. The best thing is to <u>recycle</u> them if you can.

Revision — it's all about stringing lots of facts together...

Learn what polymerisation is and practise the set of diagrams for ethene. Also learn all the examples given for the different types of plastics. <u>Then cover the page and scribble it all down</u>.

Enzymes

Enzymes are <u>biological catalysts</u>. They're pretty useful things, as they're used to speed up reactions. And they're in your Exam too, which is as good a reason as any to know about them.

Enzymes are used for doing weird things to foods

1) The <u>proteins</u> in some <u>baby foods</u> are '<u>predigested</u>' using <u>proteases</u> (protein-digesting enzymes).

2) The <u>centres</u> of <u>chocolates</u> can be softened using enzymes.

3) <u>Carbohydrases</u> can turn <u>starch syrup</u> (yuk) into <u>sugar syrup</u> (yum) by breaking the starch (carbohydrate) down into sugar.

4) <u>Glucose syrup</u> can be turned into <u>fructose syrup</u> using <u>isomerase</u>. Fructose is <u>sweeter</u>, so you can use <u>less</u> of it — good for slimming foods and drinks.

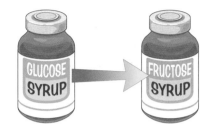

Yoghurt and Cheese making — only pasteurised milk

1) <u>Pasteurised milk</u> <u>**MUST**</u> be used for making <u>cheese</u> and <u>yoghurt</u>, because <u>fresh</u> milk contains many <u>unwanted bacteria</u> which would give them a <u>bad taste</u>.

2) Instead the pasteurised milk is mixed with <u>specially grown cultures</u> of bacteria.

3) This mixture is kept at the <u>ideal temperature</u> for the bacteria and their enzymes to work.

4) For <u>yoghurt</u> this is <u>pretty warm</u>, at about <u>45°C</u>.

5) The <u>yoghurt-making bacteria</u> convert <u>lactose</u> (the natural sugar found in milk) into <u>lactic acid</u>. This gives yoghurts their slightly <u>bitter</u> taste.

6) <u>Cheese</u> on the other hand matures better in <u>cooler conditions</u>.

7) <u>Various</u> bacterial enzymes can be used in <u>cheese-making</u> to produce different <u>textures</u> and <u>tastes</u>.

Enzymes are used in Biological Detergents

1) <u>Enzymes</u> are the '<u>biological</u>' ingredients in biological detergents and washing powders.

2) They're mainly <u>proteases</u> (protein-digesting enzymes) and <u>lipases</u> (fat-digesting enzymes).

3) Because the enzymes attack <u>animal</u> and <u>plant</u> matter, they're ideal for removing <u>stains</u> like <u>food</u> or <u>blood</u>.

This page is just so easy — it's a blummin' picnic...

Where would we be without the powers of enzymes. Not only would we be <u>hungry</u> but we would <u>smell</u> too... anyway, learn this page. It's not too hard, usual score, <u>read</u> it, <u>memorise</u> it, <u>write it down</u> and then whabam — you know it all. Then go have a wash and some cheese.

Chemical Equations

Equations need a lot of practice if you're going to get them right.
They can get real tricky real quickly, unless you really know your stuff.
Every time you do an equation you need to practise getting it right rather than skating over it.

Chemical Formulas tell you how many atoms there are

1) Hydrogen chloride has the chemical formula HCl. This means that in any molecule of hydrogen chloride there will be: <u>one</u> atom of hydrogen bonded to <u>one</u> atom of chlorine.

2) Ammonia has the formula NH_3. This means that in any molecule of ammonia there will be: <u>three</u> atoms of hydrogen bonded to <u>one</u> atom of nitrogen. Simple.

3) A chemical reaction can be described by the process reactants → products.
  eg.   methane reacts with oxygen to produce carbon dioxide and water
  eg.   magnesium reacts with oxygen to produce magnesium oxide.
You have to know how to write these reactions in both words and symbols, as shown below:

The Symbol Equation shows the atoms on both sides:

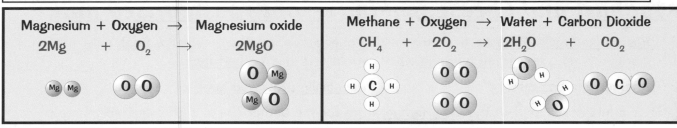

Magnesium + Oxygen → Magnesium oxide
$2Mg$ + O_2 → $2MgO$

Methane + Oxygen → Water + Carbon Dioxide
CH_4 + $2O_2$ → $2H_2O$ + CO_2

You need to know how to write out any Equation...

You really do need to know how to write out chemical equations. In fact you need to know how to write out equations for pretty well all the reactions in this book.
That might sound like an awful lot, but there aren't nearly as many as you think. Have a look.
You also need to know the formulae for all the ionic and covalent compounds in here too. Lovely.

State Symbols tell you what Physical State it's in

These are easy enough, <u>just make sure you know them</u>, especially aq (aqueous).

(s) — Solid	(l) — Liquid	(g) — Gas	(aq) — Dissolved in water

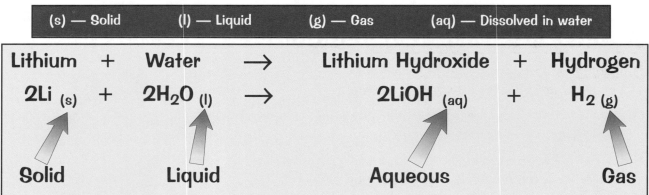

Lithium + Water → Lithium Hydroxide + Hydrogen
$2Li_{(s)}$ + $2H_2O_{(l)}$ → $2LiOH_{(aq)}$ + $H_{2(g)}$

Solid   Liquid   Aqueous   Gas

It's tricky — but don't get yourself in a state over it...

<u>Make sure</u> you know the formulae for the elements and compounds you come across in the chemistry modules. Try writing symbol equations for the following reactions, and put the state symbols in too: 1) Sodium + chlorine → sodium chloride
2) Methane + oxygen → carbon dioxide + water (See pages 38 and 45 for answers.)

Balancing Equations

Things start to get a wee bit tricky now. Hang in there and remember... practice makes perfect.

Balancing The Equation — match them up one by one

1) There must always be the <u>same</u> number of atoms on <u>both sides</u>, they can't just <u>disappear</u>.
2) You <u>balance</u> the equation by putting numbers <u>in front</u> of the formulae where needed.
   Take this equation for reacting sulphuric acid with sodium hydroxide:

$$H_2SO_4 \ + \ NaOH \ \rightarrow \ Na_2SO_4 \ + H_2O$$

The <u>formulae</u> are all correct but the numbers of some atoms <u>don't match up</u> on both sides.
You <u>can't change formulae</u> like H_2SO_4 to H_2SO_5. You can only put numbers <u>in front of them</u>:

Method: Balance just ONE type of atom at a time

The more you practise, the quicker you get, but all you do is this:

1) Find an element that *doesn't balance* and *pencil in a number* to try and sort it out.
2) *See where it gets you.* It may create *another imbalance* but pencil in *another number* and see where that gets you.
3) Carry on chasing <u>unbalanced</u> elements and it'll *sort itself out* pretty quickly.

<u>I'll show you</u>. In the equation above you soon see we're short of H atoms on the RHS (Right Hand Side).
1) The only thing you can do about that is make it $2H_2O$ instead of just H_2O:

$$H_2SO_4 \ + \ NaOH \ \rightarrow \ Na_2SO_4 \ + 2H_2O$$

2) But that now causes too many H atoms and O atoms on the RHS, so to balance that up you could try putting 2NaOH on the LHS (Left Hand Side):

$$H_2SO_4 \ + \ 2NaOH \ \rightarrow \ Na_2SO_4 \ + 2H_2O$$

3) And suddenly there it is! <u>Everything balances</u>. And you'll notice the Na just sorted itself out.

Ionic Equations — make sure the electrons balance

Ionic equations are no different really, except that you have <u>electrons and charges</u> involved as well.
The <u>total charge</u> on each side of the equation has to balance.

Example: The bond between sodium and chlorine in <u>sodium chloride</u> is ionic — a sodium atom gives a (negatively charged) electron to a chlorine atom. You can show this with <u>ionic equations</u>.

The sodium atom splits into a positive sodium ion and an electron...

$$Na \ \rightarrow \ Na^+ + e^-$$

$$Cl + e^- \ \rightarrow \ Cl^-$$

...and the chlorine atom gains the electron to become a negative chloride ion.

The <u>positive sodium ion</u> and the <u>negative chloride ion</u> are then pulled together by their opposite charges.

Ionic equations are also used to describe what happens in <u>electrolysis</u>. Electrolysis is covered in proper detail in <u>Module Nine</u>. Just for a laugh, here are <u>ionic equations</u> to show hydrogen and chorine being given off during electrolysis of sodium chloride solution.

H^+ ions from water gain electrons to form hydrogen gas.

$$2H^+ + 2e^- \ \rightarrow \ H_2$$

$$2Cl^- \ \rightarrow \ Cl_2 + 2e^-$$

Cl^- ions lose electrons to form chlorine gas.

Balancing equations — weigh it up in your mind...

Practise scribbling down all these details, <u>mini-essay</u> style. This stuff can be a bit confusing — I think you have to make a real effort to learn all the details. But seeing as they expect you to know this stuff for all the Chemistry modules, it's the kind of thing you really <u>need to know</u>.

Nine Types of Reaction

Types of Chemical Reactions

There are <u>nine</u> types of chemical change you should know about. It's well worth learning exactly what each of them is, <u>here and now</u>, rather than living the rest of your life in a confused haze.

1) THERMAL DECOMPOSITION — *breakdown on heating*

This is when a substance <u>breaks down</u> into simpler substances <u>when heated</u>, often with the help of a <u>catalyst</u>. It's different from a reaction because there's only <u>one substance</u> to start with. <u>Cracking of hydrocarbons</u> is a good example of thermal decomposition.

2) NEUTRALISATION — *acid + alkali gives salt + water*

This is simply when an <u>acid</u> reacts with an <u>alkali</u> (or base) to form a <u>neutral</u> product, which is neither acid nor alkali (usually a <u>salt</u> solution).

3) DISPLACEMENT — *one element kicking another one out*

This is a reaction where a <u>more reactive</u> element reacts with a compound and <u>pushes out</u> a <u>less reactive</u> "rival" element. <u>Metals</u> are the most common example. Magnesium will react with iron sulphate to push the iron out and form magnesium sulphate.

4) PRECIPITATION — *solid forms in solution*

This is a reaction where <u>two solutions react</u> and a <u>solid</u> forms in the solution and <u>sinks</u>. The solid is said to "<u>precipitate out</u>" and, confusingly, the solid is also called "<u>a precipitate</u>".

5) OXIDATION — *loss of electrons*

<u>Oxidation</u> is the <u>addition of oxygen</u>. Iron becoming iron oxide is oxidation. The more technical and general definition of oxidation is "<u>the loss of electrons</u>".

Remember "OIL RIG" (Oxidation Is Loss, Reduction Is Gain)

6) REDUCTION — *gain of electrons*

<u>Reduction</u> is the <u>reverse of oxidation</u>, ie. the <u>loss of oxygen</u>. Iron oxide is <u>reduced</u> to iron. The more technical and general definition of reduction is "<u>the gain of electrons</u>". Note that <u>reduction</u> is <u>gain</u> of electrons. That's the way to remember it — it's kinda <u>the wrong way round</u>.

7) EXOTHERMIC REACTIONS — *give out heat*

<u>Exothermic</u> reactions <u>give out energy</u>, usually as heat. "Exo-" as in "Exit", or "out". Any time a <u>fuel burns</u> and <u>gives off heat</u> it's an <u>exothermic</u> reaction.

8) ENDOTHERMIC REACTIONS — *take in heat*

<u>Endothermic</u> reactions need heat <u>putting in</u> constantly to make them work. Heat is needed to <u>form chemical bonds</u>. The <u>products</u> of endothermic reactions are likely to be <u>more useful</u> than the <u>reactants</u>, otherwise we <u>wouldn't bother putting all the energy in</u>, eg. turning <u>iron oxide</u> into <u>iron</u> is an endothermic process. We need a lot of heat from coke to keep it happening.

9) REVERSIBLE REACTIONS — *they go both ways*

<u>Reversible</u> reactions are ones that will cheerfully go in <u>both</u> directions at the <u>same time</u>. In other words, the <u>products</u> can easily turn back into the <u>original reactants</u>.

Nine more fantastic chat-up lines just waiting to happen...

<u>A nice easy page to learn</u>. You should know a lot of this already. Anyway, cover the page and expose each yellow box (without the other bit of the heading!) one by one and try to explain it to yourself before uncovering the text to check. Then a pat on the back is in order.

Important Uses of Limestone

Types of Chemical Reactions

1) Limestone for Neutralising Acid in Lakes and Soil

This is the equation for <u>any</u> neutralisation reaction. Learn it well:

> acid + alkali hydroxide solution ⟶ neutral salt solution + water

1) Neutralisation reactions can be used to make <u>fertilisers</u>:

$$HNO_3 + KOH \longrightarrow KNO_3 + H_2O$$

Potassium Nitrate (KNO_3) can be used as a fertiliser.

2) Ordinary limestone <u>ground into powder</u> can be used to <u>neutralise</u> acidity in lakes caused by <u>acid rain</u>.

3) It can also be used to neutralise <u>acid soils</u> in fields.
But it works <u>better</u> and <u>faster</u> if it's turned into <u>slaked lime</u> first.

2) Turning Limestone into Slaked Lime; First Heat it up...

1) Limestone is a <u>sedimentary rock</u>, formed mainly from <u>sea shells</u>. It's mostly <u>calcium carbonate</u>.
2) Limestone can be easily turned into <u>quicklime</u> by heating it.
3) This reaction is a <u>thermal decomposition</u>.

> limestone $\xrightarrow{\text{HEAT}}$ quicklime   or $CaCO_3 \xrightarrow{\text{HEAT}} CaO + CO_2$

4) Copper carbonate does pretty much the same thing.

> $CuCO_3 \xrightarrow{\text{HEAT}} CuO + CO_2$

...then Add Water

1) <u>Calcium oxide</u> reacts <u>violently</u> with <u>water</u> to produce <u>calcium hydroxide</u> (or <u>slaked lime</u>).

> quicklime + water ⟶ slaked lime   or $CaO + H_2O \longrightarrow Ca(OH)_2$

2) <u>Slaked lime</u> is a <u>white powder</u> and can be applied to fields just like powdered limestone.
3) The <u>advantage</u> is that slaked lime acts much <u>faster</u> to reduce the acidity.

3) Limestone is Used to Make Cement and Glass

1) <u>Clay</u> contains <u>aluminium</u> and <u>silicates</u> and is dug out of the ground.
2) Powdered <u>clay</u> and powdered <u>limestone</u> are <u>roasted</u> in a rotating <u>kiln</u> to produce a complex mixture of calcium and aluminium silicates, called <u>cement</u>.
3) When <u>cement</u> is mixed with <u>water</u> a slow chemical reaction takes place.
4) This causes the cement to gradually <u>set hard</u>.
5) Cement is usually mixed with <u>sand and chippings</u> to make <u>concrete</u>.
6) <u>Concrete</u> is a very quick and cheap way of constructing buildings — and it shows...
— concrete has got to be the most hideously unattractive building material ever known.

1) To make glass, just heat up <u>limestone</u> (calcium carbonate) with <u>sand</u> (silicon dioxide) and <u>soda</u> (sodium carbonate) until it <u>melts</u>.
2) When the mixture cools it comes out as <u>glass</u>. It's as easy as that. Eat your heart out, Mr. Pilkington.

Tough Revision here — this stuff's rock hard...

I bet when those little sea creatures died all those millions of years ago, they had no idea they would one day become the cornerstones of 20th century civilisation. Get it! — cornerstones. Chortle chortle. Anyway, enough frivolity. <u>Learn the whole page</u> till you've got it rock solid...

Revision Summary for Module Four

These questions aren't exactly friendly, but they're a seriously serious way of finding out what you don't know. And don't forget, that's what revision is all about — finding out what you don't know and then learning it till you do. Practise these questions as often as necessary — not just once. Your ultimate aim is to be able to answer all of them easily.

1) Describe how crude oil is formed. How long does this process take?

2) What does crude oil consist of?

3) Draw a full diagram showing the fractional distillation of crude oil.

4) Name seven fractions obtained from crude oil, and what they are used for.

5) What are hydrocarbons? Describe how four of their properties vary with molecule size.

6) Give the equations for complete and incomplete combustion of hydrocarbons.

7) Which type is dangerous and why? What do the flames look like for these two types of combustion?

8) What are alkanes and alkenes? What is the basic difference between them?

9) Draw the structures of the first four alkanes and the first two alkenes, and give their names.

10) List four differences between alkanes and alkenes.

11) What is "cracking"? Why is it done?

12) Give a typical example of a substance which is cracked, and the products that you get.

13) What are the industrial conditions used for cracking?

14) What are polymers? Name a group of substances that can form polymers.

15) Draw diagrams to show how ethene forms a polymer.

16) Name four types of plastic, give their physical properties and say what they're used for.

17) Give one reason why it is an especially good idea to try and recycle plastics.

18) List four things that food manufacturers use enzymes for.

19) Describe how enzymes are used in cheese and yoghurt making.

20) What's your favourite cheese?

21) Describe why enzymes in biological detergents are good at removing stains.

22) Balance the following chemical equations:

$$\text{a)} \quad Mg + O_2 \longrightarrow MgO \qquad \text{b)} \quad C_2H_4 + O_2 \longrightarrow CO_2 + H_2O$$

23) Name nine different types of chemical change.

24) Is oxidation loss or gain of electrons?

25) What is the big word for a reaction that gives out heat?

26) What two products do we get from a neutralisation reaction?

27) Give the equations for turning limestone into slaked lime. Why do we bother?

28) What kind of reaction is involved when limestone is turned into quicklime?

29) Describe how cement is made, and how it can be used to make concrete.

Circuits — The Basics

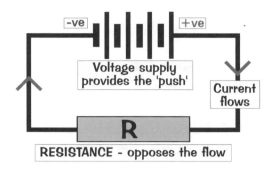

Electricity — bad news if you don't know the basics. Don't even <u>think</u> about skipping this bit.

1) **CURRENT** is the <u>flow</u> of electrons round the circuit.
   Current will <u>only flow</u> through a component if there is
   a <u>voltage</u> across that component.

2) **VOLTAGE** is the <u>driving force</u> that pushes the
   current round.   Kind of like '<u>electrical pressure</u>'.

3) **RESISTANCE** is anything in the circuit
   which <u>slows the flow down</u>.

4) **There's a BALANCE:** the <u>voltage</u> is trying to <u>push</u>
   the current round the circuit, and the <u>resistance</u> is
   <u>opposing</u> it — the <u>relative sizes</u> of the voltage and
   resistance decide <u>how big</u> the current will be:

> If you *increase the VOLTAGE* — then *MORE CURRENT* will flow.
> If you *increase the RESISTANCE* — then *LESS CURRENT* will flow.

Circuit Symbols You Should Know:

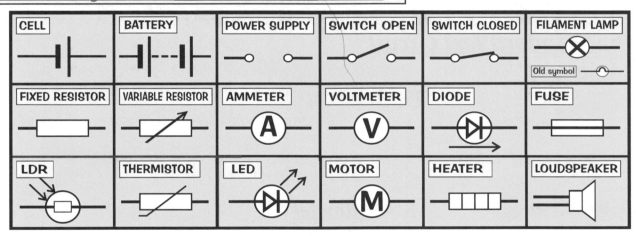

CELL	BATTERY	POWER SUPPLY	SWITCH OPEN	SWITCH CLOSED	FILAMENT LAMP
FIXED RESISTOR	VARIABLE RESISTOR	AMMETER	VOLTMETER	DIODE	FUSE
LDR	THERMISTOR	LED	MOTOR	HEATER	LOUDSPEAKER

Alternating and Direct Current

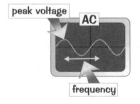

1) In an <u>AC supply</u> (alternating current), the current is <u>constantly</u>
   changing direction. The voltage is constantly going up and down.
   The <u>cathode ray oscilloscope</u> (CRO) trace is <u>always a wave</u>.

2) Not surprisingly with a <u>DC supply</u> (direct current), the current
   keeps flowing in the <u>same direction</u>. The voltage is constant.
   The <u>CRO trace</u> is a <u>horizontal line</u>. <u>Batteries</u> and <u>cells</u> provide DC supply.

You need to <u>learn</u> these CRO traces — I've not put them in cos they're pretty.

Understanding currents — easy as pie...

Before you go any further, make sure you know this stuff — what <u>voltage</u>, <u>current</u> and
<u>resistance</u> are, the <u>circuit symbols</u>, and the difference between <u>AC</u> and <u>DC</u>. Get your head
round this now and the rest will be a lot easier. Learn the definitions, then cover the page and
see how many you can <u>scribble</u> down — keep going until you can remember them all easily.

Resistors and Thermistors

Circuits

Plenty of electrical stuff here — you need to know <u>all of it</u>.

1) Variable Resistor

1) A <u>resistor</u> whose resistance can be <u>changed</u> by twiddling a knob or something.
2) The old-fashioned ones are huge coils of <u>wire</u> with a <u>slider</u>.
3) Turn the resistance <u>up</u>, the current <u>drops</u>.
   Turn the resistance <u>down</u>, the current goes <u>up</u>.
4) <u>Variable</u> resistors are great for <u>altering</u> the <u>current</u> flowing through a circuit.

2) Light Dependent Resistor or 'LDR' to you

1) In <u>bright light</u>, the resistance <u>falls</u>.
2) In <u>darkness</u>, the resistance is <u>highest</u>.
3) This makes it a useful device for various <u>electronic circuits</u>,
   eg. <u>automatic night lights</u>, <u>burglar detectors</u>.

3) Thermistor (Temperature-dependent Resistor)

1) In <u>hot</u> conditions, the resistance <u>drops</u>.
2) In <u>cool</u> conditions, the resistance goes <u>up</u>.
3) Thermistors make useful <u>temperature detectors</u>,
   eg. <u>car engine</u> temperature sensors and electronic <u>thermostats</u>.

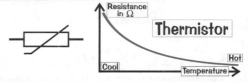

The Standard Test Circuit

This is without doubt the most totally bog-standard circuit the world has ever known. So know it.

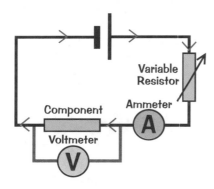

The Ammeter

1) Measures the <u>current</u> (in <u>Amps</u>) flowing through the component.
2) Must be placed <u>in series</u>.
3) Can be put <u>anywhere</u> in series in the <u>main circuit</u>,
   but <u>never in parallel</u> like the voltmeter.

The Voltmeter

1) Measures the <u>voltage</u> (in <u>Volts</u>) across the component.
2) Must be placed <u>in parallel</u> around the <u>component</u>
   — <u>NOT</u> around the variable resistor or the battery!
3) The <u>proper</u> name for "<u>voltage</u>" is "<u>potential difference</u>" or "<u>PD</u>".

Five Important Points

1) This <u>basic circuit</u> is used for <u>testing components</u>, and for getting <u>V-I graphs</u> for them. (See next page).
2) The <u>component</u>, the <u>ammeter</u> and the <u>variable resistor</u> are all <u>in series</u>, which means they can be put <u>in any order</u> in the main circuit. The <u>voltmeter</u>, on the other hand, can only be placed <u>in parallel</u> around the <u>component under test</u>, as shown. Anywhere else is a definite <u>no-no</u>.
3) As you <u>vary</u> the <u>variable resistor</u> it alters the <u>current</u> flowing through the circuit.
4) This allows you to take several <u>PAIRS OF READINGS</u> from the <u>ammeter</u> and <u>voltmeter</u>.
5) You can <u>plot</u> these values for <u>current</u> and <u>voltage</u> on a <u>V-I graph</u>, like the ones on the next page.

Standard circuit, standard dreariness...

Make sure that you know everything here. Don't forget the <u>standard circuit</u> — learn how it's set up, then <u>cover</u> the page and <u>scribble</u> it down until you can remember all the details.

Resistance and V=I×R

Circuits

This is what you'd actually use the <u>standard test circuit</u> for — to get these little beauties.
I love it when a plan comes together.

Four Hideously Important Voltage-Current (V-I) Graphs

<u>V-I graphs</u> show how the <u>current</u> varies as you change the <u>voltage</u>. Learn these four real well:

| Resistor | Different Wires | Filament Lamp | Diode |

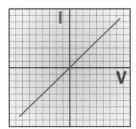 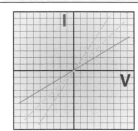 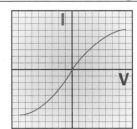 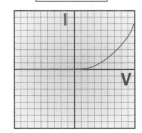

The current through a <u>resistor</u> (at constant temperature) is <u>proportional to voltage</u>.

<u>Different wires</u> have different <u>resistances</u>, hence the different <u>slopes</u>.

As the <u>temperature</u> of the filament <u>increases</u>, the <u>resistance increases</u>, hence the <u>curve</u>.

Current will only flow through a diode <u>in one direction</u>, as shown.

Calculating Resistance: R =V/I, (or R ='1/gradient')

1) For the <u>straight-line graphs</u> the resistance of the component is <u>steady</u> and is equal to the <u>inverse</u> of the <u>gradient</u> of the line, or '<u>1/gradient</u>'. In other words, the <u>steeper</u> the graph the <u>lower</u> the resistance.

2) If the graph <u>curves</u>, it means the resistance is <u>changing</u>. In that case R can be found for any point by taking the <u>pair of values</u> (V,I) from the graph and sticking them in the formula <u>R =V/I</u>. Easy.

$$\text{Resistance} = \frac{\text{Potential Difference}}{\text{Current}}$$

Calculating Resistance — An Example

EXAMPLE. Voltmeter V reads 6V and resistor R is 4Ω, what is the current through ammeter A?

ANSWER. Taking the formula V = I×R, we need to find I so the version we need is I = V/R. The answer is then 6/4, which is 1½ A.

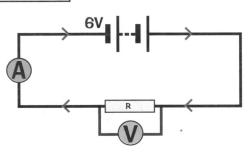

In the end, you'll have to learn this — resistance is futile...

There are quite a lot of important details on this page and you need to <u>learn all of them</u>. The only way to make sure you really know it is to <u>cover up the page</u> and see how much of it you can <u>scribble down</u> from <u>memory</u>. Sure, it's not that easy — but it's the only way. Enjoy.

Mains
Electricity

Electricity at Home

I have electricity in my house. It's great. I use it for lights. I also use it for my television.

Mains Supply is AC

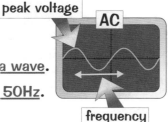

peak voltage

AC

frequency

1) The U.K. mains supply is 230 – 240 Volts.

2) It's an AC supply (alternating current), so its CRO trace would be a wave.

3) The frequency of the AC mains supply is 50 cycles per second or 50Hz.
(Hz stands for Hertz.)

All Resistors produce Heat when a Current flows through them

1) Whenever a current flows through anything with electrical resistance
(which is almost everything), electrical energy is converted into heat energy.

2) The more current that flows, the more heat is produced.

3) A bigger voltage means more heating, because it pushes more current through.

4) Also the higher the resistance, the less heat is produced. This is because a
higher resistance means less current will flow, and that reduces the heating.

5) This heating effect is used in electric bar heaters, immersion heaters, kettles, cookers and irons.

Hazards in The Home — Eliminate Them before They Eliminate You

Mains electricity provides a current which can injure or kill you — and it'd be nice to avoid this.
A possible Exam question will show you a picture of domestic bliss but with various
electrical hazards in the picture such as kids shoving their fingers into sockets and stuff like
that, and they'll ask you to list all the hazards. This should be mostly common sense, but it
won't half help if you've already learnt this list:

1) Long cables or frayed cables.

2) Cables in contact with something hot or wet.

3) Pet rabbits or children (always hazardous).

4) Water near sockets
(or shoving things in sockets).

5) Damaged plugs, or too many plugs
into one socket.

6) Lighting sockets without bulbs in.

7) Appliances without their covers on.

Some people are so careless with electricity — it's shocking...

Ouch, 240V would be really be quite painful. I know that the safety stuff is pretty simple,
but check that you know the facts. The same goes for all the other stuff here. Ho hum...

Plugs and Cables

Mains Electricity

This is definitely going to be useful to know — after all, you've got an exam soon.

Plugs and Cables — Learn the Safety Features

Get the Wiring Right

1) No bare wires showing inside the plug.
2) Cable grip tightly fastened over the cable outer layer.
3) The right coloured wire connected to each pin, and firmly screwed in.
4) The fuse in the live conductor — a safety device to prevent current surges and electrocution.

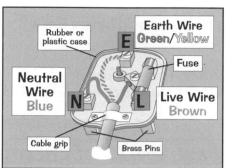

Plug Features

1) The metal parts are made of copper or brass because these are very good conductors.
2) The case, cable grip and cable insulation are all made of plastic because this is a really good insulator and is flexible too.
3) This all keeps the electricity flowing where it should.

Earthing and Fuses Prevent Fires and Shocks

The LIVE WIRE alternates between a HIGH +VE AND –VE VOLTAGE, with an average of about 230V. The NEUTRAL WIRE is always at 0V and is needed to make a complete circuit.

Electricity normally flows in and out through the live and neutral wires only. The EARTH WIRE and fuse are just for safety and work together like this:

1) If a fault develops in which the live somehow touches the metal case, then because the case is earthed, a big current flows in through the live, through the case and out down the earth wire.
2) This surge in current (above the fuse rating) causes the fuse wire to heat and melt (the fuse blows).
3) When the fuse blows the circuit breaks and the live supply cuts. The appliance becomes isolated making it impossible to get an electric shock from the case. It also prevents the risk of fire caused by the heating effect of a large current.
4) Fuses should be rated as near as possible but just higher than the normal operating current.

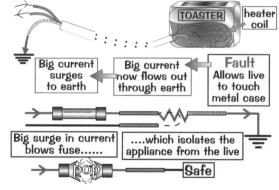

Extra Safety — Double Insulation and Circuit Breakers

1) If the appliance has a plastic casing and no metal parts showing, it's said to be DOUBLE INSULATED. Anything with double insulation just needs a live and a neutral wire. Household products like drills, hairdryers and vacuum cleaners have double insulation.

2) A Residual Current Circuit Breaker (RCCB) also prevents electrocution. Normally exactly the same current flows through the live and neutral wires. If someone touches the live wire and a current flows through them to Earth, then the neutral wire has less current than the live wire. An RCCB detects this difference and quickly cuts the power. RCCB's can easily be reset by flicking a switch on the device.

Learn about electricity — it's shocking stuff...

Make sure you learn the wiring for a plug, and how fuses and the earth wire stop everything from going wrong. There's worse stuff than this to be honest, so make the effort to learn the facts, then cover the page and away you go. You can't afford to skimp on the revision.

Electrical Power

Mains Electricity

Electricity is <u>powerful</u> stuff, but really simple once you get the hang of it.
It's pretty likely that you'll be asked a question like these, so learn how to do 'em...

Calculating Fuse ratings

The <u>fuse</u> needed for a particular appliance should have a rating
slightly <u>higher</u> than the <u>current</u> that the item will use.

<u>Example</u>: *A hairdryer is rated at 2.6A. Find the fuse needed.*
<u>ANSWER</u>: If the normal current is 2.6A, then a 3 amp fuse will be ideal.

Kilowatt-hours (kW-h) are 'UNITS' of Energy

Your electricity meter counts the number of '<u>UNITS</u>' of energy used —
otherwise known as a <u>kilowatt-hour</u>, or <u>kW-h</u>. A '<u>kW-h</u>' might sound like a
unit of power, but it's not — it's an <u>amount of energy</u>. Learn this definition.

> A **KILOWATT-HOUR** is the amount of electrical energy
> used by a **1 KW APPLIANCE** left on for **1 HOUR**.

The Easy Formula for Calculating The Cost of Electricity

This must surely be the most <u>trivial and obvious</u> formula you'll ever see.
Anyway, it's in the <u>syllabus</u> so here you go:

<u>Cost</u> = <u>Power</u> (in kW) × <u>Time</u> (in hours) × <u>Cost of 1 kWh</u>

N.B. Always turn the <u>power</u> into <u>kW</u> (not Watts) and the <u>time</u> into <u>hours</u> (not minutes)

Example one: Richard watches a 2 hour film on a 0.5 kW television.
If one kilowatt-hour costs 10p, how much does it cost
Richard to watch the film?

<u>Answer</u>: Cost = Power x Time x Cost of 1 kWh.
Cost = 0.5 x 2 x 10p = 10p.

Example two: A 500 W kettle takes 12 minutes to boil. If one kilowatt-hour
costs 10p, how much does it cost to boil the kettle?

<u>Answer</u>: This is almost the same as before — except for the <u>units</u>.
Convert 12 minutes into hours, and watts into kilowatts.
Cost = Power x Time x Cost of 1 kWh.
Cost = (500/1000) x (12/60) x 10p = 1p.

> 12 minutes = 12/60 = 0.2 hours
> 500 watts = 0.5 kW

Kilowa Towers — the best lit hotel in Hawaii...

That's it — all you need to know about calculating <u>fuse ratings</u> and <u>electricity bills</u> is here.
You don't need to remember the cost equation as it'll be given to you in the exam. Always
always always remember to use the <u>right units</u> though — the wrong units will get you the <u>wrong
answer</u>. Check that your answer looks <u>reasonable</u>. There's no point in <u>throwing marks away</u>.

Generators and Transformers

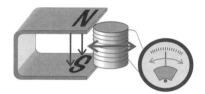

Energy
Resources

Generators and transformers both use electromagntic induction. Sounds terrifying.
Well sure it's quite mysterious, but it isn't that complicated:

> ELECTROMAGNETIC INDUCTION: The creation of VOLTAGE (and maybe current)
> in a wire which is experiencing a CHANGE IN MAGNETIC FIELD.

For some reason they use the word 'induction' rather than 'creation', but it means the same thing.

EM Induction — a) Field Cutting b) Field Through a Coil

Electromagnetic induction is the induction of a voltage and/or current in a conductor.
There are two different situations where you get EM induction. You need to know both of them:
  a) The conductor moves across a magnetic field and 'cuts' through the field lines.
  b) The magnetic field through a closed coil changes, ie. gets bigger or smaller or reverses.

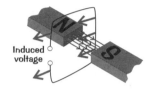

Induced voltage

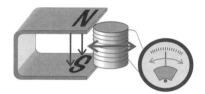

Generators and Dynamos

1) Dynamos and generators are basically the same
   thing — they both create an electric current in a
   coil of wire, using electromagnetic induction.
2) Dynamos rotate a magnet inside the coil, whereas
   generators rotate the coil around the magnet.
   The output from dynamos and generators is AC
   — as shown in the CRO displays below.

Generators and dynamos vary
quite a bit in shape and size
— from small bike dynamos
to the monsters that
generate mains electricity.

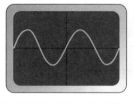 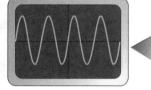

Different frequencies come
from rotating the magnet/coil
at different speeds.

Transformers Change the Voltage — but only AC Voltages

Transformers use Electromagnetic Induction.
That means they'll only work on AC.
1) A transformer consists of two coils of wire
    wrapped around an iron coil.
2) Step-up transformers step the voltage up.
    They have more turns on the secondary coil.
3) Step-down transformers step the voltage down.
    They have fewer turns on the secondary coil.
    Step-down transformers drop the voltage from
    400,000V (for transmission across the country) to a nice 'safe' 240V for our homes.

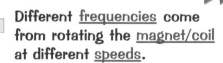

Laminated iron core

Primary coil

Secondary coil

Will this transform your life...

This is probably the hardest section of the syllabus, but also one of the most important. Start by
learning all the facts on generators and dynamos, and then move onto transformers. When you
think you've learnt it all, write a mini-essay to test yourself. Keep trying until you know it all.

Energy
Resources

National Grid

1) The <u>National Grid</u> is the <u>network</u> of pylons and cables which <u>covers</u> the whole country.

2) It takes electricity from the <u>power stations</u>, to just where it's needed in <u>homes</u> and <u>industry</u>.

3) It enables power to be <u>generated</u> anywhere on the grid, and to then be <u>supplied</u> anywhere else on the grid.

<u>Learn</u> all these features of the <u>national grid</u> — power stations, transformers, pylons, and voltages.

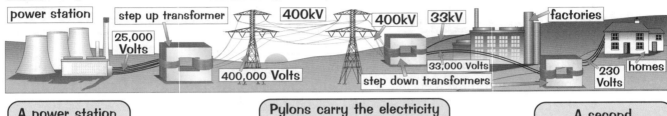

A power station generates electricity at 25,000V. → A transformer steps the voltage up from 25,000V to 400,000V. → Pylons carry the electricity across the country. → The voltage is reduced to 33,000V for use in factories and buildings. → A second transformer reduces the voltage to around 240V for home use.

Pylon Cables are at 400,000 V to keep the Current Low

You need to understand why the <u>voltage</u> is so <u>high</u> and why it's <u>AC</u>. Learn these points.

1) The formula for <u>power supplied</u> is: <u>Power = Voltage × Current</u> or: <u>P = V×I</u>.

2) So to transmit a <u>lot</u> of power, you either need high <u>voltage</u> or high <u>current</u>.

3) The problem with <u>high current</u> is the <u>loss</u> (as heat) due to the <u>resistance</u> of the cables.

4) It's much <u>cheaper</u> to boost the voltage up to <u>400,000V</u> and keep the current <u>very low</u>.

5) This requires <u>transformers</u> as well as <u>big</u> pylons with <u>huge</u> insulators, but it's still <u>cheaper</u>.

6) The transformers have to <u>step</u> the voltage <u>up</u> at one end, for <u>efficient</u> transmission, and then bring it back down to <u>safe</u> levels at the other end.

7) This is why it has to be <u>AC</u> on the National Grid — so that the <u>transformers</u> will work!

Overhead or Underground Cables — which are best?

There are basically two types of national grid cable — overhead between pylons or buried underground.

<u>Overhead cables are...</u>	<u>Underground cables are...</u>
1) <u>Naturally cooled</u> — air stops the wires from getting too hot.	1) <u>Expensive</u> — they aren't cooled and have to be <u>very thick</u> to prevent <u>overheating</u>.
2) <u>Easy</u> to <u>access</u> and <u>repair</u>.	2) <u>Unreliable</u> — they're a nightmare to <u>repair</u>.
3) Quick and easy to <u>build</u> across the country.	3) <u>Hard to build</u> — it's <u>expensive</u> and <u>time consuming</u> to dig trenches for the cables.
4) A real <u>eyesore</u> — they ruin the <u>scenery</u>.	4) <u>Mostly hidden</u> — you ain't gonna see them.

400,000 Volts? — that could give you a buzz...

Make sure you can explain why <u>power cables</u> are at <u>400,000 V</u>. It's pretty straightforward stuff once you know the key points, so make sure you learn them. Also take the time to learn the features of the <u>National Grid</u> — I know it's not mind blowing stuff but it's on the <u>syllabus</u>. Final thing — learn the <u>four</u> points on <u>overhead</u> and <u>underground</u> cables so you know what you're talking about in the exam. <u>Cover and scribble</u>... And as always, <u>enjoy</u>.

Energy Resources

Energy Resources

The energy we use comes from loads of different sources — some renewable, some non-renewable.

Non-renewable Energy Resources Will Run Out One Day

The non-renewables are the three fossil fuels and nuclear:

1) Coal
2) Oil
3) Natural gas
4) Nuclear fuels (uranium and plutonium)

a) They will all run out one day.
b) They all do damage to the environment.
c) But they provide most of our energy.

Renewable Energy Resources Will Never Run Out

The renewables are:

1) Wind
2) Waves
3) Tides
4) Hydroelectric
5) Solar
6) Geothermal
7) Biomass (wood)

a) These will never run out.
b) They do not damage the environment (except visually).
c) The trouble is they don't provide much energy and many of them are unreliable because they depend on the weather.

Comparison of Renewables and Non-Renewables

1) They're quite likely to give you an Exam question asking you to "evaluate" or "discuss" the relative merits of generating power by renewable and non-renewable resources.
2) The way to get the marks is to simply list the pros and cons of each method.
3) Full details are given on the next few pages. However there are some clear generalisations you should definitely learn to help answer such questions. Make sure you can list these from memory:

Non-Renewable Resources (Coal, Oil, Gas and Nuclear)

ADVANTAGES:

1) High output.
2) Reliable output.
3) Don't take up much land.
4) Can match demand for power.

DISADVANTAGES:

1) Very polluting.
2) Involve mining or drilling, and transportation of fuel.
3) They are running out quite quickly.
4) High cost of building (and dismantling) power stations.

Renewable Resources (Wind, Waves, Solar etc.)

ADVANTAGES:

1) No pollution.
2) No fuel costs (although high initial costs).

DISADVANTAGES:

1) Require large areas of land or water and often spoil the landscape.
2) They don't always deliver when needed — if the weather isn't right, for example.

Stop fuelling around and learn this stuff properly...

This is dead simple — make sure that you can list the general advantages and disadvantages of renewable and non-renewable energy sources. Just cover the page and scribble them down...

Energy Resources

Power from Non-Renewables

Most of the electricity we use is generated from the four NON-RENEWABLE sources of energy (coal, oil, gas and nuclear) in big power stations, which are all pretty much the same apart from the boiler.

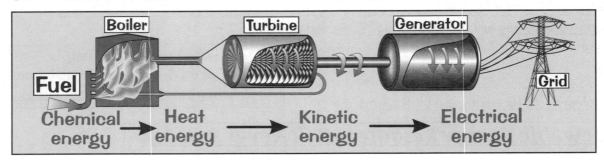

Nuclear Reactors are Just Fancy Boilers

1) A nuclear power station is mostly the same as the one shown above, where heat is produced in a boiler to make steam to drive turbines etc. The difference is in the boiler, which is just a tad more complicated, as shown here.

2) They take the longest time of all the non-renewables to start up — it takes ages to build the power plants and check that they're safe.

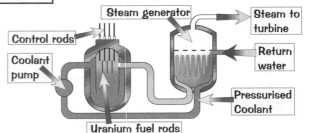

Environmental Problems With The Use Of Non-Renewables

1) All three fossil fuels, (coal, oil and gas) release CO_2. For the same amount of energy, coal releases the most CO_2, followed by oil then gas. All this CO_2 adds to the Greenhouse Effect, causing global warming. There's no feasible way to stop it being released either. Ho hum.

2) Burning coal and oil releases sulphur dioxide, which causes acid rain.

3) Coal mining makes a mess of the landscape, especially 'open-cast mining'.

4) Oil spills cause serious environmental problems. We try to avoid it, but it'll always happen.

5) Nuclear power is clean but the nuclear waste is very dangerous and difficult to dispose of.

6) Nuclear fuel (ie. uranium) is cheap but the overall cost of nuclear power is high due to the cost of the power plant and final de-commissioning.

7) Nuclear power always carries the risk of a major catastrophe like the Chernobyl disaster.

The Non-Renewables Need to be Conserved

1) When the fossil fuels eventually run out we'll have to use other forms of energy.

2) More importantly however, fossil fuels (especially crude oil) are also a very useful source of chemicals, which will be hard to replace when they're all gone.

3) To stop the fossil fuels running out so quickly there are two things we can do:

1) Use Less Energy by Being More Efficient With it:

(i) Better insulation of buildings,
(ii) Turning lights and other things off when not needed,
(iii) Making everyone drive spiddly little cars with diddly little engines.

2) Use More Of The Renewable Sources Of Energy

as detailed on the next two pages...

Learn about the non-renewables — before it's too late...

Make sure you realise that we generate most of our electricity from the four non-renewables, and the power stations are all pretty much the same, ie. like the one in the diagram. Also make sure you know all the problems about them and why we should use less of them.

Power from Renewables

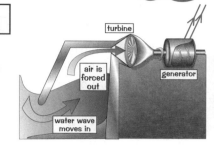

Wave Power — Lots of little Wave Converters

1) You need lots of small <u>wave generators</u> located <u>around the coast</u>.
2) As waves come in to the shore they provide an <u>up and down motion</u> which can be used to drive a <u>generator</u>.
3) They are <u>fairly unreliable</u>, since waves tend to die out when the <u>wind drops</u>.
4) The main environmental problem is <u>spoiling the view</u>.
5) You may get asked about <u>energy transfer chains</u>, so learn this example.

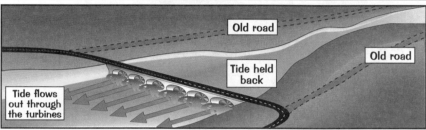

SUN ⇒	heats atmosphere ⇒	creates WINDS ⇒	and WAVES ⇒	ELECTRICITY
	(HEAT ENERGY)	(KINETIC ENERGY)		(ELECTRICAL ENERGY)

Tidal Barrages — Using The Sun and Moon's Gravity

1) <u>Tidal barrages</u> are <u>big dams</u> built across river <u>estuaries</u> with <u>turbines</u> in them.
2) As the tide <u>comes in</u> it fills up the estuary to a height of <u>several metres</u>. This water can then be allowed out through <u>turbines</u> at a controlled speed. It also drives the turbines on the way in.
3) The main problems are <u>preventing free access by boats</u>, <u>spoiling the view</u> and <u>altering the habitat</u> of the wildlife, eg. wading birds, sea creatures and beasties who live in the sand.
4) Tides are pretty <u>reliable</u> in the sense that they happen <u>twice a day</u> without fail, and always to the <u>predicted height</u>. The only drawback is that the <u>height</u> of the tide is <u>variable</u> so lower (<u>neap</u>) tides will provide significantly <u>less energy</u> than the bigger <u>spring</u> tides. But tidal barrages are excellent for <u>storing energy</u> ready for periods of <u>peak demand</u>.

Hydroelectricity — using Dams

1) <u>Hydroelectric power</u> usually requires the <u>flooding</u> of a <u>valley</u> by building a <u>big dam</u>.
2) <u>Rainwater</u> is caught and allowed out <u>through turbines</u>. There is <u>no pollution</u>.
3) There is quite a <u>big impact</u> on the <u>environment</u> due to the flooding of the valley and possible <u>loss of habitat</u> for some species. The reservoirs can also look very <u>unsightly</u> when they <u>dry up</u>. Location in <u>remote valleys</u> (in <u>Scotland</u>) tends to avoid these problems on the whole.

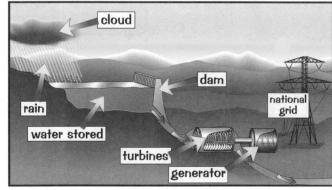

4) A <u>big advantage</u> is <u>immediate response</u> to increased demand and there's no problem with <u>reliability</u> except in times of <u>drought</u> — but remember this is Scotland we're talking about!
5) <u>Initial costs are high</u> but there's <u>no fuel</u> and <u>minimal running costs</u>.

Learn about Wave Power — and bid your cares goodbye...

There are loads of ways to use <u>water</u> to generate electricity. Make sure that you know the <u>advantages</u> and <u>disadvantages</u> of each by covering the page and <u>scribbling</u> away...

Power from Renewables

Energy Resources

Wind Power — Lots of Little Wind Turbines

1) This involves putting lots of <u>windmills</u> (wind turbines) up in <u>exposed places</u> like on <u>moors</u> or around <u>coasts</u>.
2) Each wind turbine has its own <u>generator</u> inside it so the electricity is generated <u>directly</u> from the <u>wind</u> turning the <u>blades</u>, which turn the <u>generator</u>. There's <u>no pollution</u>.
3) But they do <u>spoil the view</u>. You need about <u>5000</u> <u>wind turbines</u> to replace one <u>coal-fired</u> power station and 5000 of them cover <u>a lot</u> of ground — that wouldn't look very nice at all.
4) There's also the problem of <u>no power when the wind stops</u>, and it's <u>impossible</u> to <u>increase supply</u> when there's <u>extra demand</u>.
5) Wind power has a similar energy transfer chain to wave power.

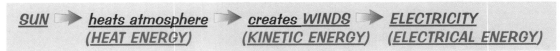

SUN ➤ _heats atmosphere_ ➤ _creates WINDS_ ➤ _ELECTRICITY_
(HEAT ENERGY) _(KINETIC ENERGY)_ _(ELECTRICAL ENERGY)_

Solar Energy — Solar Cells and Solar Panels

Solar Cells:

1) <u>SOLAR CELLS</u> generate <u>electric currents directly</u> from sunlight. <u>Initial costs</u> are <u>high</u> but after that the energy is <u>free</u> and <u>running costs almost nil</u>.
2) Despite the cost, solar cells are the <u>best</u> source of energy for <u>calculators</u> and <u>watches</u>, which don't use much electricity. Solar power is the only choice for <u>remote places</u> like <u>Antarctica</u>.
3) There's absolutely <u>no pollution</u> — and in sunny countries solar power is a <u>very reliable</u> source of energy — but only in the <u>daytime</u>.

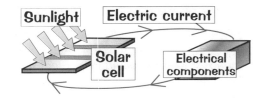

The <u>energy transfer chain</u> for <u>solar cells</u>:

SUN ➤ _light_ ➤ _ELECTRICITY_
(LIGHT ENERGY) _(ELECTRICAL ENERGY)_

Solar Panels:

1) <u>SOLAR PANELS</u> are less sophisticated. They heat water. The <u>black surface</u> absorbs heat, and heats the <u>pipes</u>.
2) Solar panels have by far the <u>easiest energy chain</u>.

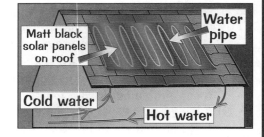

SUN ➤ _heat energy_
(HEAT ENERGY)

Solar Cells are like Fried Eggs — always best sunny side up...

There's an awful lot of <u>details</u> here on sources of energy. Trouble is, in the Exam they could test you on <u>any</u> of them, so I guess you just gotta <u>learn 'em all</u> — including the <u>energy transfer</u> chains. A few <u>mini-essays</u> might be just what the doctor ordered, I think.

Saving power

There are many types of insulation used in houses to reduce energy loss.
Read on to find out about them...

Air — it's a great insulator

1) A lot of heat energy is lost by conduction and convection.
2) Lots of insulating materials, like fibre glass wool, have large pockets of air in them.
3) Air's a very good insulator, so heat transfer by conduction is greatly reduced.
4) Also, convection currents can't form in the material because the air is trapped and can't move around.

Home Insulation is all about Stopping the Movement of Air

like these ones, for example...

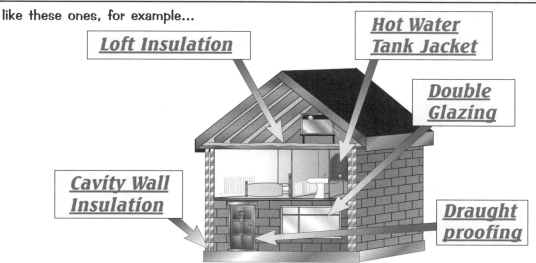

Loft Insulation

Hot Water Tank Jacket

Double Glazing

Cavity Wall Insulation

Draught proofing

Know Which Types of Heat Transfer are Involved:

1) These types of insulation reduce the transfer of energy between objects at different temperatures.

2) Cavity Wall Insulation — foam in the gap between the bricks reduces convection and radiation.

3) Loft insulation — a thick layer of fibre glass wool laid out across the whole loft floor reduces conduction and radiation into the roof space from the ceiling.

4) Draught proofing — strips of foam and plastic around doors and windows reduce heat loss due to convection.

5) Double Glazing — two layers of glass with an air gap reduce conduction and radiation.

6) Hot water tank jacket — fibre glass wool reduces conduction and radiation from the hot water tank.

Know the benefits of saving energy

Home insulation and energy saving appliances, like low energy light bulbs, have two main benefits.

1) They save you money in the long run. Home insulation can be very expensive, but in the long run you save money as you use less energy. Low energy light bulbs give out as much light as normal bulbs but use less electricity.

2) They help the environment. We're still using a lot of non-renewable energy sources. If we use less energy, there'll be less pollution — and also our natural resources will last longer.

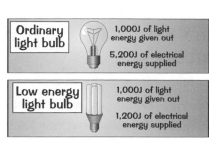

Ordinary light bulb — 1,000J of light energy given out, 5,200J of electrical energy supplied

Low energy light bulb — 1,000J of light energy given out, 1,200J of electrical energy supplied

They don't seem to have these problems in Spain...

This is a nice topic to finish the section — most of it is common sense, but just make sure you can scribble down all of the key points easily. Then go and have a cup of tea.

Revision Summary for Module Five

To get to grips with Physics you have to get used to learning about things which you can't see. Try these questions and see how well you're doing. If you manage them then everything's just peachy. If you struggle at all, try them again after taking another squiz at the Module.

1) Describe what current, voltage and resistance are.
2) Scribble down 18 circuit symbols that you know, with their names of course.
3) How do voltage and resistance affect current?
4) What type of current do batteries and cells provide? Is it the same as the mains supply?
5) Sketch out the standard test circuit with all the details. Describe how it's used.
6) Write down two facts about: a) LDR   b) thermistor   c) variable resistor.
7) Sketch the V-I graphs for a resistor and a diode, and explain their shapes.
   How do you calculate R from them?
8) Find the voltage when a current of 0.5 A flows through a resistance of 10 Ω.
9) Find: a) The current when a resistance of 96 Ω is connected to a battery of 12 V.
           b) The voltage when a current of 0.25 A passes through a resistance of 54 Ω.
10) What happens to a resistor when a current flows through it? What appliances make use of this?
11) Write down six potential electrical hazards in the home.
12) Draw a diagram of a properly wired plug with all the labels.
13) What wires does a plug need if it has double insulation?
14) Explain how earthing and fuses work — where is the fuse placed in the plug?
15) How does a residual current circuit breaker work?
16) Write down the formula connecting the power of an appliance and the cost of the electricity it uses.
17) Give the definition of electromagnetic induction. Outline two cases where it happens.
18) Outline how generators and dynamos work.
19) Describe the two types of transformer and the main difference between them.
20) Why are transformers used on the National Grid?
21) What are the advantages of using renewable over non-renewable energy resources?
22) Give two advantages of using low energy appliances.
23) Describe two ways that water is used to generate electricity.
24) Describe the differences between solar panels and solar cells.
25) Why do most insulating materials have air trapped in them?
26) Copy the diagram of the house on the right and label the insulating materials that could be used to prevent energy loss.

Types of Wave

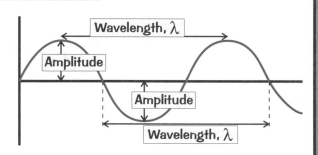

Waves are <u>different</u> from anything else. They have various features which <u>only</u> waves have:

Amplitude, Wavelength **and** Frequency

1) The <u>amplitude</u> goes from the <u>middle</u> line to the <u>peak</u>, **NOT** from a trough to a peak.

2) The <u>wavelength</u> covers a <u>full cycle</u> of the wave, eg. from <u>peak to peak</u>, not just from *"two bits that are sort of separated a bit"*. It's measured in metres (m).

3) <u>Frequency</u> is how many <u>complete waves</u> there are <u>per second</u> (passing a certain point). It's measured in Hertz (Hz) — <u>50Hz</u> means that <u>50</u> waves pass a certain point each <u>second</u>.

Transverse Waves **have** Sideways Vibrations

<u>Most waves</u> are <u>transverse</u>:

1) <u>Light</u> and all other <u>electromagnetic radiation</u>.
2) <u>Ripples</u> on water.
3) Waves on <u>strings</u>.
4) A <u>slinky spring</u> wiggled up and down.

In <u>transverse waves</u> the vibrations are at <u>90°</u> to the <u>direction of travel</u> of the wave.

Vibrations from side to side   Wave travelling this way

Longitudinal Waves **have** Vibrations along the Same Line

The <u>only longitudinal waves</u> are:

1) <u>Sound</u> — It travels as a longitudinal wave through solids, liquids and gases.
2) <u>Shock waves</u> eg. seismic waves.
3) A <u>slinky spring</u> when plucked.

In <u>longitudinal waves</u> the vibrations are <u>along the same direction</u> as the wave is travelling.

One wavelength   Rarefactions   Vibrations in same direction   as wave is travelling

Compressions

<u>Don't</u> get confused by CRO displays which show a <u>transverse wave</u> when displaying <u>sounds</u>. The real wave is <u>longitudinal</u> — the display shows a transverse wave so you know <u>what's going on</u>.

All Waves Carry Energy

1) <u>Light</u>, <u>infra red</u>, and <u>microwaves</u> all make things <u>warm up</u>. <u>X-rays</u> and <u>gamma rays</u> can cause <u>ionisation</u> and <u>damage</u> to cells, which also shows that they <u>carry energy</u>.
2) <u>Loud sounds</u> make things <u>vibrate or move</u>. Even very quiet sounds can move your <u>ear drum</u>.
3) Waves on the sea can <u>toss big boats around</u> and can <u>generate electricity</u>.
4) Waves also transfer <u>information</u>, as well as energy, eg. TV, radio, speech, fibre optics, etc.

Learn about waves — just get into the vibes, man...

There's not much to learn here really, and it's all very basic stuff on waves. Four sections with some tasty titbits in each. <u>Learn</u> the headings, then all of the details. Once you've done that <u>cover up the page</u> and see what you can <u>scribble down</u>. Keep trying until you can remember the whole lot easily from memory. It's all just <u>easy marks to be won</u>... <u>or lost</u>.

The Electromagnetic Spectrum

Waves

There are Seven Basic Types of Electromagnetic Wave

We split Electromagnetic waves (EM waves) into <u>seven</u> basic types as shown below.
These EM waves form a <u>continuous spectrum</u> so the different regions do actually <u>merge</u> into each other.

RADIO WAVES	MICRO WAVES	INFRA RED	VISIBLE LIGHT	ULTRA VIOLET	X-RAYS	GAMMA RAYS
$1m-10^4m$	$10^{-2}m$ (3cm)	$10^{-5}m$ (0.01mm)	$10^{-7}m$	$10^{-8}m$	$10^{-10}m$	$10^{-12}m$

Our <u>eyes</u> can only detect a very <u>narrow range</u> of EM waves, which are the ones we call (visible) <u>light</u>.
All EM waves are transverse waves which travel at <u>exactly</u> the same <u>speed</u> as light in a <u>vacuum</u>, and
<u>pretty much</u> the same speed as light in <u>other media</u> like glass or water — though this is always <u>slower</u>
than their speed in a vacuum.

As the Wavelength Changes, So Do The Properties

1) As the <u>wavelength</u> of EM radiation changes, its <u>interaction</u> with matter changes. In particular the way any EM wave is <u>absorbed</u>, <u>reflected</u> or <u>transmitted</u> by any given substance depends <u>entirely</u> on its <u>wavelength</u> — that's the whole point of these pages of course!
2) When <u>any</u> EM radiation is <u>absorbed</u> it can cause <u>two effects</u>:
   a) <u>Heating</u>   b) Creation of a tiny <u>alternating current</u> with the <u>same</u> frequency as the radiation.
3) The <u>higher the frequency</u> (or shorter the wavelength), the <u>higher the energy</u> of the wave. High energy waves can cause more harm, and are more <u>dangerous</u>.

Radio Waves are Used Mainly For Communications

1) <u>Radio Waves</u> are used mainly for <u>communication</u>.
2) Both <u>TV and FM Radio</u> use <u>short wavelength</u> radio waves of about <u>1m wavelength</u>.
3) To receive these wavelengths you need to be more or less in <u>direct sight</u> of the transmitter, because they will <u>not</u> bend (diffract) over hills or travel very far <u>through</u> buildings.
4) The <u>longer wavelengths</u> (like medium wave radio signals) can travel further because they are <u>reflected</u> from an <u>electrically charged layer</u> in the Earth's upper atmosphere (the ionosphere). This means they can be sent further around the Earth.

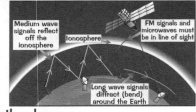

Microwaves Are Used For Cooking and Satellite Signals

1) <u>Microwaves</u> have <u>two</u> main uses: <u>cooking</u> food and <u>satellite</u> transmissions.
2) Satellite transmissions use a frequency of microwaves which passes <u>easily</u> through the <u>Earth's atmosphere</u>, including <u>clouds</u>, which seems sensible.
3) The frequency used for <u>cooking</u>, on the other hand, is one which is readily <u>absorbed</u> by <u>water molecules</u>. The microwaves pass easily into the <u>food</u> and are then <u>absorbed</u> by the <u>water molecules</u> and turn into heat <u>inside</u> the food.
4) Microwaves can be <u>dangerous</u> because they can be absorbed by <u>living tissue</u> and the <u>internal heating</u> will <u>damage or kill</u> the cells causing a sort of '<u>cold burn</u>'.

 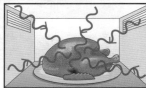

The spectrum — isn't that something kinda rude in Biology...

There are lots of details on this page that you definitely need to know. The top diagram is an absolute must — they usually give it you with one or two missing labels to be filled in. <u>Learn</u> the four sections on this page then <u>scribble</u> a <u>mini-essay</u> for each one to see what you know.

The Electromagnetic Spectrum

Waves

Visible light is Used To See With and In Optical Fibres

Visible light is pretty useful. It's used in <u>Optical Fibre Digital Communications</u>, <u>photography</u> and <u>endoscopes</u>, which are the best ones for your answer in the <u>Exam</u>.

Infrared Radiation — Toasters and Remote Controls

1) <u>Infrared</u> (or IR) is otherwise known as <u>heat radiation</u>. This is given out by all <u>hot</u> objects and you <u>feel it</u> on your <u>skin</u> as <u>radiant heat</u>. Infrared is readily <u>absorbed</u> by <u>all</u> materials and causes <u>heating</u>.
2) <u>Radiant heaters</u> (ie. those that <u>glow red</u>) use infrared radiation, including <u>toasters</u> and <u>grills</u>.
3) <u>Over-exposure</u> to infrared causes <u>damage</u> to cells.
4) Infrared is used in <u>security systems</u>, <u>night vision devices</u>, <u>remote controls</u> of <u>TVs and videos</u>, and to treat <u>muscular problems</u>.

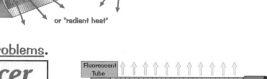

Heat radiation or "radiant heat"

infra red

Ultraviolet Light Causes Skin Cancer

1) This is what causes <u>skin cancer</u> if you spend <u>too</u> much time in the <u>sun</u>. Overexposure will damage surface cells and your eyes.
2) It also causes your skin to <u>tan</u>. <u>Sunbeds</u> give out UV rays but <u>less harmful</u> ones than the Sun does.
3) <u>Darker skin</u> protects against UV rays by <u>preventing</u> them from reaching more vulnerable <u>skin tissues</u> deeper down.
4) There are special <u>coatings</u> which <u>absorb</u> UV light and then give out <u>visible light</u>. These are used to coat the inside of <u>fluorescent tubes</u> and lamps.
5) Ultra violet is also useful for hidden <u>security marks</u> which are written in special ink that can only be seen with an ultraviolet light. It is also used to detect <u>forged bank notes</u>.

Fluorescent Tube | UV light produced inside tube
Coating on glass absorbs UV and emits visible light

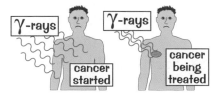

X-Rays Are Used in Hospitals, but are Pretty Dangerous

1) These are used in <u>hospitals</u> to take <u>X-ray photographs</u> of people to see whether they have any <u>broken bones</u>.
2) X-rays pass through <u>flesh</u> but not through <u>denser material</u> such as <u>bones</u> or <u>metal</u>.
3) X-rays can damage cells and cause <u>cancer</u>, so <u>radiographers</u>, who take X-ray pictures <u>all day long</u>, wear <u>lead aprons</u> and stand behind a <u>lead screen</u> to <u>minimise</u> their <u>exposure</u>.

Gamma Rays Cause Cancer but Are Used to Treat it Too

1) Gamma Rays are used to kill <u>harmful bacteria</u> in food to keep it <u>fresher</u> for longer.
2) They are also used to <u>sterilise medical instruments</u>, again by killing the <u>bacteria</u>.
3) They can also be used in the <u>treatment of cancer</u> because they <u>kill cancer cells</u>.
4) Gamma rays tend to pass <u>through</u> soft tissue but <u>some</u> are <u>absorbed</u> by the cells.
5) In <u>high doses</u>, gamma rays (along with X-rays and UV rays) can <u>kill normal cells</u>.
6) In <u>lower doses</u> all these three types of EM Waves (UV, X-rays and gamma rays) can cause normal cells to become <u>cancerous</u>.

Gamma source

γ-rays | γ-rays
cancer started | cancer being treated

Radiographers are like teachers — they can see right through you...

Here are the other five parts of the EM spectrum for you to learn. Ace, isn't it. At least there's some groovy diagrams to help relieve the tedium. On this page there are five sections.
Do a <u>mini-essay</u> for each section, then <u>check</u>, <u>re-learn</u>, <u>re-scribble</u>, <u>re-check</u>, etc. etc.

Waves

Refraction

1) *Refraction Is always Caused By the Waves Changing Speed*

1) When waves <u>slow</u> down they change in <u>wavelength</u> (but <u>not frequency</u>), and bend <u>towards</u> the normal.

2) When <u>light</u> enters <u>glass</u> it <u>slows</u> down to about <u>2/3</u> of its speed in air.

3) When waves hit the boundary <u>along a normal</u>, ie. at <u>exactly 90°</u>, then there will be <u>no change</u> in direction — this is <u>important</u>. There'll still be a change in <u>speed</u> and <u>wavelength</u>, though.

4) <u>Some</u> light is also <u>reflected</u> when light hits a <u>different medium</u> such as glass.

5) <u>Sound</u> refracts too...

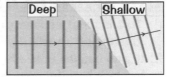

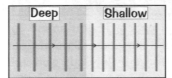

<u>Sound</u> will also refract (change direction) as it enters <u>different media</u>. However, since sound is always <u>spreading out</u> so much, the change in direction is <u>hard</u> to spot. Just remember, sound <u>does</u> refract. The fact that sound and light are both refracted gives further <u>evidence</u> that they travel as <u>waves</u>.

2) *Refraction is Shown by Waves in a Ripple Tank Slowing Down*

1) The waves travel <u>slower</u> in <u>shallower water</u>, causing <u>refraction</u> as shown.

2) There's a change in <u>direction</u>, and a change in <u>wavelength</u> but <u>NO change</u> in <u>frequency</u>.

3) *Refraction of Light — The Good Old Glass Block Demo*

You can't fail to remember the old "<u>ray of light</u> through a <u>rectangular glass block</u>" trick. Make sure you can draw this diagram from <u>memory</u>, with every detail <u>perfect</u>.

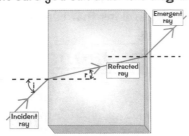

1) Take <u>careful</u> note of the positions of the <u>normals</u> and the <u>exact</u> positions of the angles of <u>incidence</u> and <u>refraction</u> (and note it's the angle of <u>refraction</u> — not <u>reflection</u>).

2) Most important of all remember <u>which way</u> the ray <u>bends</u> — <u>towards</u> the normal as it enters the <u>denser medium</u>, <u>away</u> from the normal as it emerges into the <u>less dense</u> medium.

3) Try to <u>visualise</u> the shape of the <u>wiggle</u> in the diagram — that can be easier than remembering the rule in words.

4) *Total Internal Reflection*

1) This <u>only happens</u> when <u>light</u> is <u>coming out</u> of something <u>dense</u>, like <u>glass</u> or <u>water</u> or <u>perspex</u>.

2) If the <u>angle</u> is <u>shallow enough</u> the ray <u>won't come out at all</u>, but it <u>reflects</u> back into the glass (or whatever). This is called <u>total internal reflection</u> because <u>ALL</u> of the light <u>reflects back in</u>.

3) You definitely need to learn this set of <u>THREE DIAGRAMS</u> which show the three conditions:

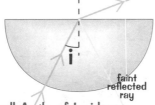

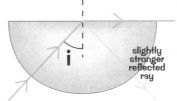

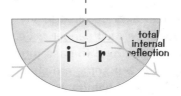

<u>Small Angle of Incidence.</u> Most of the light <u>passes through</u> into the air but a <u>little</u> bit of it is <u>internally reflected</u>.

<u>Medium Angle of Incidence.</u> The emerging ray comes out <u>along the surface</u>. There's quite a bit of <u>internal reflection</u>.

<u>Large Angle of Incidence.</u> <u>No light comes out.</u> It's <u>all</u> internally reflected, ie. <u>total internal reflection</u>.

Revise refraction — but don't let it slow you down...

The first thing you've gotta do is make sure you know what <u>causes refraction</u>. When you know that learn all of the <u>diagrams</u> about refraction and total internal reflection. This is really useful.

Analogue and Digital Signals

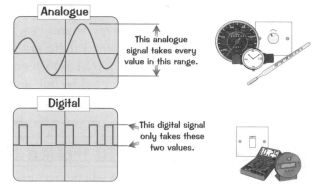

Waves

Analogue and Digital signals are pretty important — life would be pretty dull without them — no phones, no computers. Even groovy digital watches wouldn't exist.

Analogue *Varies But Digital's Either On or Off*

1) Analogue and digital signals are very different.
2) An analogue wave can take any value within a certain range. (Remember: analogue — any.)
3) A digital signal on the other hand can only take two values — on or off.
4) The two values of a digital signal are sometimes given other names — but the point is that there are only two possible values. These other names might be...
        ...true or false, 1 or 0, high or low etc.

Analogue

This analogue signal takes every value in this range.

Digital

This digital signal only takes these two values.

Signals *Have to Be Amplified*

Both digital and analogue signals weaken as they travel — so they need to be amplified along their route. They also pick up random disturbances, called noise.

'Clean' wave

Noisy wave

Digital Signals *are Far Better Quality*

1) Noise is less of a problem with digital signals. If you receive a noisy digital signal, it's pretty obvious what it's supposed to be.

This noisy digital signal... ...is obviously supposed to be this.

2) But if you receive a noisy analogue signal, it's difficult to know what the original signal would have looked like.

But this noisy analogue signal... ...could have started like this... ...or this...

3) This is why digital signals are much higher quality — the information received is the same as the original.

4) It's also much quicker to send information as a digital signal than as an analogue signal. This means that in the same time, you can send loads more information if you use digital signals.

5) Also, many digital signals can be transmitted at once by a clever way of overlapping them on the same cable or EM wave — but you don't need to learn *how* they do it. Phew.

Optical Fibres *use Total Internal Reflections*

1) Optical fibres can carry information over long distances by repeated total internal reflections. They carry the information as light or infra-red radiation.

2) Optical communications have several advantages over electrical signals in wires:
   a) a cable of the same diameter can carry a lot more information.
   b) the signals cannot be tapped into, or suffer interference from electrical sources.
   c) the signal doesn't need boosting as often because there's little energy loss in transmission.

3) The fibre must be narrow, so that the ray stays within the fibre (total internal reflection) as shown. Also, the fibre mustn't be bent too sharply.

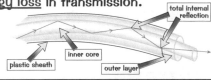

total internal reflection

plastic sheath   inner core   outer layer

Total Internal Reflection — *sounds like a Government Inquiry...*

There you go — four easy sections which give you all that you need to know about different types of signal and, of course, those optical fibre thingies. If you can do mini-essays with all the key points, and sketch a labelled picture of an optical fibre then you'll be fine...

Sound Waves

Waves

Sound travels as <u>longitudinal</u> pressure waves — they're significantly different to EM waves. Nevertheless, sound is definitely a wave so it can be <u>reflected</u> off things (producing <u>echoes</u>), and <u>refracted</u>.

The <u>Frequency</u> of a Sound Wave Determines its <u>Pitch</u>

1) <u>High frequency</u> sound waves sound <u>high pitched</u> like a <u>squeaking mouse</u>.
2) <u>Low frequency</u> sound waves sound <u>low pitched</u> like a <u>mooing cow</u>.
3) As well as <u>Hz</u>, other common units are <u>kHz</u> (1000 Hz) and <u>MHz</u> (1,000,000 Hz).
4) <u>High frequency</u> (or high pitch) also means <u>shorter wavelength</u>.
5) The range of frequencies heard by humans is from <u>20Hz</u> to <u>20,000Hz</u> (20kHz).
6) This range gradually <u>decreases</u> as we get <u>older</u>.

<u>Ultrasound</u> is Sound with a Higher Frequency than We Can Hear

Electrical devices can be made which produce <u>electrical oscillations</u> of <u>any frequency</u>. These can easily be converted into <u>mechanical vibrations</u> to produce <u>sound</u> waves <u>beyond the range of human hearing</u> (ie. frequencies above 20kHz). This is called <u>ultrasound</u> and it has some important uses:

a) <u>For</u> *Pre-Natal Scanning of a Foetus*

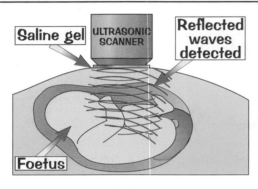

Saline gel | ULTRASONIC SCANNER | Reflected waves detected | Foetus

1) As the ultrasound hits <u>different media</u>, some of the sound wave is <u>reflected</u>.

2) These reflected waves are processed by <u>computer</u> to produce a video <u>image</u> of the foetus.

3) Ultrasound waves are used instead of <u>X-rays</u>, which would be very <u>dangerous</u> for the <u>foetus</u>.

b) *Range and Direction Finding* — SONAR

1) <u>Bats</u> send out <u>high-pitched squeaks</u> (ultrasound) and pick up the <u>reflections</u> with their <u>big ears</u>.

2) Their brains are able to <u>process</u> the reflected signal and turn it into a <u>picture</u> of what's around.

3) So the bats basically "<u>see</u>" with <u>sound waves</u> — well enough in fact to <u>catch moths</u> in <u>mid-flight</u> in complete <u>darkness</u> — it's a nice trick if you can do it.

4) The same technique is used for <u>sonar</u>, which uses <u>sound waves</u> underwater to detect features on the sea-bed.

5) The <u>pattern</u> of the reflections indicates the <u>depth</u> and basic features.

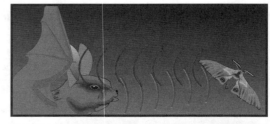

<u>Ultrasound — weren't they a pop group...</u>

Three dead simple sections for you to remember — hey I can't make it much easier than that. Remember that sound is a <u>longitudinal</u> wave and that we can only <u>hear</u> a limited <u>range</u> of frequencies. Have another read through the ultrasound stuff and then write down all the key facts — keep trying until you're sure you know it...

The Solar System

You need to learn the order of the planets, which is made easier by using the little jollyism below:

Mercury,	Venus,	Earth,	Mars,	(Asteroids),	Jupiter,	Saturn,	Uranus,	Neptune,	Pluto
(My	Very	Energetic	Maiden	Aunt	Just	Swam	Under	North	Pier)

MERCURY, VENUS, EARTH and MARS are known as the INNER PLANETS.
JUPITER, SATURN, URANUS, NEPTUNE and PLUTO are further away and are the OUTER PLANETS.
Some of the other planets in the solar system have moons orbiting them like the Moon orbits the Earth.

The Planets Don't Give Out Light, They just Reflect The Sun's

1) You can see some of the nearer planets with the naked eye at night, eg. Mars and Venus.
2) They look just like stars, but they are of course totally different.
3) Stars are huge and very far away and give out lots of light.
   The planets are smaller and nearer and they just reflect the sunlight falling on them.
4) Planets always orbit around stars. In our Solar System the planets orbit the Sun of course.
5) All the planets in our Solar System orbit in the same plane except Pluto (as shown above).
6) The further the planet is from the Sun, the longer its orbit takes.

Our Solar System is in The Milky Way Galaxy

1) The Sun is one of many millions of stars which form the Milky Way Galaxy.
2) The distance between neighbouring stars is usually millions of times greater than the distance between planets in our Solar System. The Milky Way is 100,000 light years across.
3) Gravity is of course the force which keeps the stars together in a galaxy and, like most things in the Universe, the galaxies all rotate, kinda like a catherine wheel only much slower.
4) Our Sun is out towards the end of one of the spiral arms of the Milky Way galaxy.

The Whole Universe has More Than A Billion Galaxies

1) Galaxies themselves are often millions of times further apart than the stars are within a galaxy.
2) So even the slowest amongst you will soon begin to realise that the Universe is mostly empty space and is really really big. Have you ever been to the NEC? Yeah? Well, it's even bigger than that.

Galaxies, The Milky Way — it's just like a big chocolate factory...

All makes you feel a bit insignificant, doesn't it? Read it again, then write out the key points.

Space

Comets and Gravity

This is one of the nicer topics in Physics. Enjoy it while it lasts.

Comets Orbit the Sun, but have very Eccentric (elongated) Orbits

Comet

1) Comets only appear every few years because their orbits take them very far from the Sun and then back in close, which is when we see them.

2) The Sun is not at the centre of the orbit, but near to one end as shown.

3) Comet orbits can be in different planes from planet orbits.

4) Comets are made of ice and rock and as they approach the Sun the ice melts leaving a bright tail of debris which can be millions of km long.

5) The comet travels much faster when it's nearer the Sun than it does when it's in the more distant part of its orbit. This is because the pull of gravity makes it speed up as it gets closer, and then slows it down as it gets further away from the Sun.

Gravity is the Force which Keeps Everything in Orbit

1) Gravity is a force of attraction which acts between all masses.
   It causes the planets and comets to orbit the Sun.

2) With very large masses like stars and planets, the force is very big and acts a long way out.

3) The closer you get to a planet, the stronger the force of attraction.

4) To counteract the stronger gravity, the planet must move faster and cover its orbit quicker.

5) Comets are also held in orbit by gravity, as are moons and satellites and space stations.

6) The size of the force of gravity follows the fairly famous "inverse square" relationship.
   The main effect of this is that the force decreases very quickly with increasing distance.
   The formula is $F \propto 1/d^2$, but I reckon it's easier just to remember the basic idea in words:

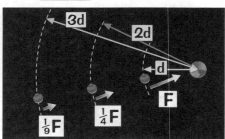

a) If you DOUBLE the distance from a planet, the size of the force will decrease by a factor of FOUR (2^2).

b) If you TREBLE the distance, the force of gravity will decrease by a factor of NINE (3^2), and so on.

c) On the other hand, if you get TWICE as close the gravity becomes FOUR times stronger.

The larger the mass of a planet, the stronger the gravitational field strength (force of gravity) on it. So there is less gravity on the Moon than Earth because the Moon has less mass than Earth. This gravitational field strength is measured in Newtons per kilogram (N/kg).
Huge planets like Jupiter have stronger gravity because they have more mass than the Earth.

Learn about these lumps of rock — and watch out for them...

Don't let gravity become a drag — just learn what you need to know... the difference between a comet's orbit and a planet's, why objects stay in orbit, and why gravity changes in different places. It's all here — read the page and write mini-essays until you can remember it all.

The Life Cycle of Stars

Space

Stars go through <u>many traumatic stages</u> in their lives — just like teenagers.

Clouds of Dust and Gas

1) Stars <u>initially form</u> from clouds of <u>dust and gas</u>.

Protostar

2) The <u>force of gravity</u> makes the dust particles come <u>spiralling in together</u>. As they do, <u>gravitational energy</u> is converted into <u>heat energy</u> and the <u>temperature rises</u>.

Main Sequence Star

3) When the <u>temperature</u> gets <u>high enough</u>, <u>hydrogen nuclei</u> undergo <u>nuclear fusion</u> to form <u>helium nuclei</u> and give out massive amounts of <u>heat and light</u>. A star is born. It immediately enters a long <u>stable period</u> where the <u>heat created</u> by the nuclear fusion provides an <u>outward pressure</u> to <u>balance</u> the <u>force of gravity</u> pulling everything <u>inwards</u>. In this stable period it's called a <u>main sequence star</u> and it lasts about <u>10 billion years</u>.
(The <u>Earth</u> has already had <u>half its innings</u> before the Sun <u>engulfs</u> it!)

4) Eventually the <u>hydrogen</u> begins to <u>run out</u> and the star then <u>swells</u> into a <u>Red Giant</u>. It becomes <u>red</u> because the surface <u>cools</u>.

5) A <u>small star</u> like our Sun will then begin to <u>cool</u> and <u>contract</u> into a <u>white dwarf</u> and then finally, as the light <u>fades completely</u>, it becomes a <u>black dwarf</u>.
(That's going to be really sad.)

Red Giant

Small stars → White Dwarf → Black Dwarf

Big stars

6) <u>Big stars</u> however, start to <u>glow brightly again</u> as they undergo more <u>fusion</u> and <u>expand and contract several times</u> forming <u>heavier elements</u> in various <u>nuclear reactions</u>. Eventually they <u>explode</u> in a <u>supernova</u>.

new planetary nebula... ...and a new solar system

Supernova

Neutron Star...

7) The <u>exploding supernova</u> throws the outer layers of <u>dust and gas</u> into space leaving a <u>very dense core</u> called a <u>neutron star</u>. If the star is <u>big enough</u> this will become a <u>black hole</u>.

...or Black Hole

8) The <u>dust and gas</u> thrown off by the supernova will form into <u>second generation stars</u> like our Sun. The <u>heavier elements</u> are <u>only</u> made in the <u>final stages</u> of a <u>big star</u> just before the final <u>supernova</u>. The <u>presence</u> of heavier elements in our <u>Sun</u> and the <u>inner planets</u> is <u>clear evidence</u> that our beautiful and wonderful world, with its warm sunsets and fresh morning dews, has all formed out of the snotty remains of a grisly old star's last dying sneeze. Lovely.

9) The <u>matter</u> from which <u>neutron stars</u> and <u>white dwarfs</u> and <u>black dwarfs</u> are made is <u>millions of times denser</u> than any matter on Earth because the <u>gravity is so strong</u> it even crushes the <u>atoms</u>.

Twinkle Twinkle little star, How I wond.. — JUST LEARN IT PAL...

Erm. Just how do they know about the whole life cycle of stars, when they're all billions and billions of km away. It's just an outrage. For your Exam, you only really need to know what happens to smaller stars — but the other stuff's just too <u>interesting</u> to leave out. Isn't it.

Space

The Universe

The Big Bang Theory of the Universe is currently the most convincing. There's also the Steady State theory which is quite presentable but it doesn't explain some of the observed features too well.

Red-shift and Background Radiation need Explaining

There are THREE important bits of evidence you need to know about:

1) Light From Other Galaxies is Red-Shifted

1) When we look at light from distant galaxies we find that all the frequencies are shifted towards the red end of the spectrum.
2) In other words the frequencies are all slightly lower than they should be. It's the same effect as a car horn sounding lower-pitched when the car is travelling away from you. The sound drops in frequency.
3) This is called the Doppler effect.
4) Measurements of the red-shift suggest that all the galaxies are moving away from us very quickly — and it's the same result whichever direction you look in.

Bye

2) The Further Away a Galaxy is, The Greater The Red-Shift

1) More distant galaxies have greater red-shifts than nearer ones.
2) This means that more distant galaxies are moving away faster than nearer ones.
3) The inescapable conclusion appears to be that the whole Universe is expanding.

3) There's a Uniform Microwave Radiation From All Directions

1) This low frequency radiation comes from all directions and from all parts of the Universe.

2) It's known as the background radiation (of the Big Bang). It's nothing to do with radioactive background radiation on Earth.

3) For complicated reasons this background radiation is strong evidence for an initial Big Bang, and as the Universe expands and cools, so this background radiation "cools" and drops in frequency.

The Steady State Theory of the Universe — Not Popular

1) This is based on the idea that the Universe appears pretty much the same everywhere and always has done.
2) In other words the Universe has always existed and always will in the same form that it is now.
3) This theory explains the apparent expansion of the Universe by suggesting that matter is being created in the spaces as the Universe expands.
4) However, as yet, there's no convincing explanation of where this new matter comes from.
5) There isn't much support for the Steady State theory, especially since the discovery of background radiation, which fits in much better with the idea of a Big Bang.
6) But you just never know...

Steady State Theory — it's just a bit pants, isn't it...

Make sure you can explain why the Steady State Theory is well dodgy.
Try writing a couple of mini-essays, it might be boring, but it works — so do it.

The Universe

The Big Bang Theory — Well Popular

1) Since all the galaxies appear to be <u>moving apart</u> very rapidly, the <u>obvious conclusion</u> is that there was an <u>initial explosion</u> — the <u>Big Bang</u>.
2) All the matter in the Universe must have been <u>compressed into a very small space</u> and then it <u>exploded</u> and the <u>expansion</u> is still going on.
3) The Big Bang is believed to have happened around <u>15 billion years ago</u>.
4) The age of the Universe can be <u>estimated</u> from the <u>current rate of expansion</u>.
5) These estimates are <u>not very accurate</u> because it's hard to tell how much the expansion has <u>slowed down</u> since the Big Bang.
6) The rate at which the expansion is <u>slowing down</u> is an <u>important factor</u> in deciding the <u>future</u> of the Universe.

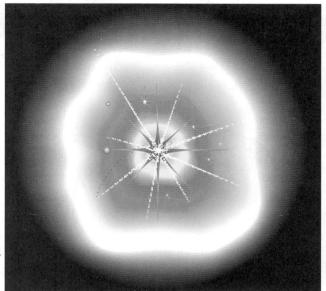

7) <u>Without gravity</u> the Universe would expand at the <u>same rate forever</u>.
8) However, the <u>attraction</u> between all the mass in the Universe tends to <u>slow</u> the expansion down.

The Future of the Universe:

It Could Expand Forever — or Collapse into The Big Crunch

1) The eventual fate of the Universe depends on <u>how fast the galaxies are moving apart</u> and how much <u>total mass</u> there is in it.
2) We can <u>measure</u> how fast the galaxies are <u>separating</u> quite easily, but we'd also like to know just <u>how much mass</u> there is in the Universe in order to <u>predict the future</u> of it.
3) This is proving <u>tricky</u> as most of the mass appears to be <u>invisible</u>, eg. <u>black holes</u>, <u>big planets</u>, <u>interstellar dust</u> etc.
Anyway, <u>depending on how much mass there is</u>, there are <u>two ways</u> the Universe could go:

1) Le Crunch — But Only if there's Enough Mass

If there's <u>enough mass</u> compared to <u>how fast</u> the galaxies are currently moving, the Universe will eventually <u>stop expanding</u> and <u>begin contracting</u>. This would end in a <u>Big Crunch</u>. The Big Crunch could be followed by another Big Bang and then <u>endless cycles</u> of <u>expansion and contraction</u>.

2) If there's Too Little Mass — then it's Le Miserable Eternity

If there's <u>too little mass</u> in the Universe to slow the expansion down, then it could <u>expand forever</u> with the Universe becoming <u>more and more spread out</u> into eternity. This seems <u>way too dismal</u> for my liking. I much prefer the idea of the Universe going <u>endlessly in cycles</u>. But what was there <u>before</u> the Universe? Or what is there <u>outside</u> of it? It's <u>mindboggling</u>.

Time and Space — it's funny old stuff isn't it...

I think it's great they've put all this stuff on space in the syllabus. I mean wow, something in Physics that's actually interesting. The great thing about learning a few bits and bobs about the Universe is that it can make you sound dead clever when you tell people about it. "Ah well, it's all to do with the diminishing Doppler red-shift over the last 15 billion years," you can say.

Life Beyond Earth

Space

Scientists look for life beyond Earth in many ways. Fortunately you only
need to know about a couple of them. Read on...

1) SETI Looks for Radio Signals from Other Planets

1) Us Earthlings are constantly beaming <u>radio</u>, <u>TV</u> and <u>radar</u> into space for any passing aliens to detect. There might be life out there that's as clever as we are. Or even cleverer. They may have built <u>transmitters</u> to send out signals like ours.

2) <u>SETI</u> stands for "Search for Extra Terrestrial Intelligence". Scientists on the SETI project are looking for <u>narrow bands</u> of <u>radio wavelengths</u> coming to Earth from outer space. They're looking for <u>meaningful signals</u> in all the 'noise'.

3) Signals on a narrow band can <u>only</u> come from a <u>transmitter</u>. The 'noise' comes from giant stars and gas clouds.

4) It takes <u>ages</u> to analyse all the radio waves, so the SETI folk get help from the public — you can download a <u>screen saver</u> off the internet which analyses a chunk of radio waves.

5) SETI has been going for the last <u>40 years</u> but they've <u>not found anything</u>. Not a sausage. ☹

6) Scientists are now looking for possible <u>laser</u> signals from outer space. Watch this space...

2) Robots Collect Photos and Samples

1) Scientists have sent robots in spacecraft to <u>Europa</u> (one of Jupiter's moons) to look for microorganisms. And robots were sent to Mars during the <u>Viking</u> missions.

2) The robots wander round the planet or moon, sending <u>photographs</u> back to Earth or collecting <u>samples</u> for analysis.

3) Scientists can detect living things or <u>evidence</u> of them, such as <u>fossils</u> or <u>remains</u>, in the samples. The "fossil" shown here is from Mars, though no one really seems sure *what* it is.

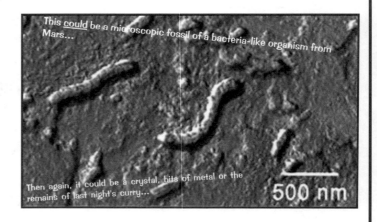

This <u>could</u> be a microscopic fossil of a bacteria-like organism from Mars...

Then again, it could be a crystal, bits of metal or the remains of last night's curry...

500 nm

4) OK, so a couple of bacteria is a bit boring but that's how we started out on Earth...

Searching for new life forms? — try looking under your SETI...

Oooh — so that's how people look for life beyond Earth. Examiners have been known to ask the odd question or two about this topic, so it's worth having another read through and making sure you remember the key facts. <u>SETI</u> is dead simple — a load of people trying to find meaningful patterns in a load of noise. And the robots — well, they're easy. <u>Cover</u> the page and write down what you remember — and <u>keep trying</u> until you've got them all.

Atoms and Isotopes

Atoms

The structure of atoms is real simple. I mean, gee, there's nothing to them. Just learn and enjoy.

Atomic structure

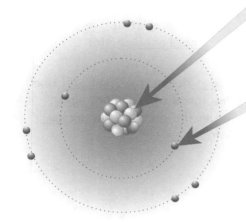

The **NUCLEUS** contains protons and neutrons.
Most of the mass of the atom is contained in the nucleus, but it takes up virtually no space — it's tiny.

The **ELECTRONS** fly around the outside.
They're negatively charged and really really small.
They occupy a lot of space and this gives the atom its size, even though it's mostly empty space.
The number of electrons is equal to the number of protons.
This means that the whole atom has no overall charge.

THE MASS NUMBER
— Total of Protons and Neutrons
(Also known as the Nucleon Number)

$^{7}_{3}$Li

THE ATOMIC NUMBER
— Number of Protons
(Also known as the Proton Number)

Points to note

1) The proton number (or atomic number) tells you how many protons there are in the nucleus.
2) This is also equal to the number of electrons in a neutral atom.
3) To get the number of neutrons subtract the proton number from the mass number.
4) The mass number is always the bigger number. It tells you the relative mass of the atom.
5) The mass number is always roughly twice the proton number.
6) This means there's about the same number of protons as neutrons in any nucleus.

Isotopes are Different Forms of The Same Element

1) All atoms of a particular element have the same number of protons.
2) Isotopes are atoms with the same number of protons but a different number of neutrons.
3) This means they have the same atomic number, but different mass number.
4) Carbon-12 and Carbon-14 are good examples.
5) Most elements have different isotopes but there's usually only one or two stable ones.
6) Radioisotopes are radioactive isotopes, which means they decay into other elements and give out radiation.
This is where all radioactivity comes from — unstable radioactive isotopes undergoing nuclear decay and spitting out high energy particles.

$^{12}_{6}$C $^{14}_{6}$C

two extra neutrons

Make atoms into nice shapes — iso-topiary...

Interesting stuff — well maybe not, but that doesn't mean it ain't important, cos it is. Once you've got this, the rest of the stuff in this section will be a lot easier. You've got to know what atomic number and mass number are, and what they physically mean. When you think you've got it, cover the page and scribble down what you know — keep going until you get it all.

Atoms

Radiation

Radioactivity is a Totally Random Process

Unstable nuclei will decay and in the process give out radiation. This process is entirely random. This means that if you have 1000 unstable nuclei, you can't say when any one of them is going to decay, and neither can you do anything at all to make a decay happen.
Each nucleus will just decay quite spontaneously in its own good time. It's completely unaffected by physical conditions like temperature or by any sort of chemical bonding etc.

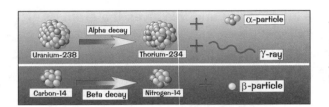

When the nucleus does decay it will spit out one or more of the three types of radiation, alpha, beta or gamma, and in the process the nucleus will often change into a new element.

Alpha Particles are Helium Nuclei ^4_2He

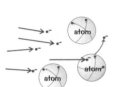

1) They're made of two protons and two neutrons so they're relatively big, heavy and slow moving. That means they don't penetrate into materials but are stopped quickly.
2) Because of their size they are strongly ionising, which just means they bash into a lot of atoms and knock electrons off them before they slow down, which creates lots of ions — hence the term "ionising".
3) An α-particle has a mass of 4 and charge of +2.
   This diagram shows a typical alpha-emission:

$$^{226}_{88}\text{Ra} \longrightarrow \ ^{222}_{86}\text{Rn} \ + \ ^4_2\text{He}$$

Beta Particles are High Energy Electrons $^0_{-1}\text{e}$

1) These are in between alpha and gamma in terms of their properties.
2) For every β-particle emitted, a neutron turns to a proton in the nucleus.
3) They move quite fast and are quite small (they're electrons).
4) They penetrate moderately before colliding, and are moderately ionising too.
5) A β-particle has no mass and a charge of -1.

A typical beta-emission:

$$^{14}_{6}\text{C} \longrightarrow \ ^{14}_{7}\text{N} \ + \ ^0_{-1}\text{e}$$

Gamma Rays are Very Short Wavelength EM Waves

1) After an alpha or beta emission the nucleus sometimes has extra energy to get rid of. It does this by emitting a gamma ray.
2) Their properties are the opposite of alpha particle properties in a way.
3) They penetrate a long way into materials without being stopped.
4) This means they are weakly ionising because they tend to pass through rather than collide with atoms. Eventually they hit something and do damage.
5) A γ-ray has no mass and no charge.
6) Gamma emission never changes the proton or mass numbers of the nucleus.

A typical combined α – and γ–emission:

$$^{238}_{92}\text{U} \longrightarrow \ ^{234}_{90}\text{Th} \ + \ ^4_2\text{He} \ + \ ^0_0\gamma$$

Learn the three types of radiation — it's easy as abc...

Alpha, beta and gamma. You do realise those are just the first three letters of the Greek alphabet don't you: α, β, γ — just like a, b, c. They might sound like complex names to you but they were just easy labels at the time. Anyway, learn all the facts about them — and scribble.

Uses of Radiation

Atoms

As radiation passes <u>through</u> materials some of the radiation is <u>absorbed</u>.
The greater the <u>thickness</u> of material the <u>more absorption</u> occurs.

<u>Alpha particles</u> are blocked by <u>paper</u>.
<u>Beta particles</u> are blocked by thin <u>aluminium</u>.
<u>Gamma rays</u> are blocked by <u>thick lead</u>.

| Thin mica | Skin or paper stops ALPHA | Thin aluminium stops BETA | Thick lead stops GAMMA |

Of course anything <u>equivalent</u> will also block them,
eg. <u>skin</u> will stop <u>alpha</u>, but <u>not</u> the others; a thin
sheet of <u>any metal</u> will stop <u>beta</u>; and very <u>thick concrete</u> will stop <u>gamma</u> just like lead does.

Thickness Control in Industry and Manufacturing

1) A <u>radioactive source</u> is directed through <u>paper</u>, <u>cardboard</u>, <u>metal</u> etc.
2) The <u>detector</u> is on the <u>other side</u> and is connected to a <u>control unit</u>.
3) When the amount of radiation detected <u>falls</u> it means the material is <u>too thick</u>, so the control unit
   pinches the rollers to make it <u>thinner</u> again.

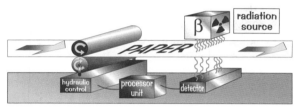

4) If the reading goes <u>up</u> it means it's <u>too thin</u>, so the
   control unit opens the rollers <u>out</u> a bit.
5) The most important thing is the <u>choice of isotope</u>.
   It must have a long <u>half-life</u> (of several <u>years</u> at least!) so
   that it emits roughly the same amount of radiation over
   time. Otherwise the strength would quickly <u>decline</u> and
   the control unit would keep <u>pinching</u> the rollers.

6) The source must be a <u>beta source</u> for <u>paper</u> and <u>cardboard</u>, or a <u>gamma source</u> for
   <u>metal sheets</u>. This is because the stuff being made must <u>partly</u> block the radiation — if it <u>all</u> goes
   through (or <u>none</u> of it does), then the reading <u>won't change</u> as the thickness changes.
   Alpha particles are no use for this since they would <u>all be stopped</u>.

Sterilisation of Food and Surgical Instruments Using γ-Rays

1) <u>Food</u> can be exposed to a <u>high dose</u> of <u>gamma rays</u>
   which will <u>kill</u> all <u>microbes</u> thus keeping the food
   <u>fresh for longer</u>.
2) <u>Medical instruments</u> can be <u>sterilised</u> in the
   same way, rather than <u>boiling them</u>.
3) The great <u>advantage</u> of <u>irradiation</u> over boiling is that
   it doesn't involve <u>high temperatures</u>, so things like
   <u>fresh apples</u> or <u>plastic instruments</u> can
   be <u>sterilised</u> without <u>damaging</u> them.

unsterilised   Gamma source   sterilised

4) The food is <u>NOT</u> radioactive afterwards, so it's <u>perfectly safe</u> to eat.
5) The isotope used for this needs to be a <u>very strong</u> emitter of <u>gamma rays</u> with a
   <u>reasonably long half-life</u> (at least several months) so that it doesn't need <u>replacing</u> too often.

Smoke detectors

1) A <u>weak</u> radioactive source is placed in the detector, close to <u>two electrodes</u>.
2) The source causes <u>ionisation</u>, and a <u>current</u> flows as a result.
3) If there's a fire then smoke will <u>absorb</u> the radiation — the current stops and the <u>alarm sounds</u>.

Will any of that be in your exam? — isotope so...

Radiation — sometimes a good thing, sometimes a bad thing. It's dead important to know
the <u>penetrating power</u> of the different types of radiation, but you need to learn the facts on
<u>thickness control</u>, <u>sterilisation</u> and <u>smoke detectors</u> as well, since it could all be in the Exam.

Background Radiation

Background Radiation Comes From Many Sources

Natural background radiation comes from:

1) Radioactivity of naturally occurring <u>unstable isotopes</u> which are <u>all</u> around us — in <u>air</u>, in <u>food</u>, in <u>building materials</u> and in <u>rocks</u>.

2) Radiation from <u>space</u> (<u>cosmic rays</u>) — mostly from the <u>Sun</u>.

3) Radiation due to <u>human activity</u>, ie. <u>fallout</u> from <u>nuclear explosions</u> or <u>dumped nuclear waste</u>. But this represents a <u>tiny</u> proportion of the total background radiation.

The <u>relative proportions</u> of <u>background radiation</u>:

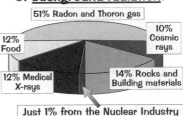

51% Radon and Thoron gas

10% Cosmic rays

12% Food

12% Medical X-rays

14% Rocks and Building materials

Just 1% from the Nuclear Industry

The level of background radiation changes, depending on where you are

1) At <u>high altitudes</u> (eg. in <u>jet planes</u>) it <u>increases</u> because of more exposure to <u>cosmic rays</u>.

Coloured bits indicate more radiation from rocks

2) <u>Underground</u> in mines, etc., it increases because of the <u>rocks</u> all around. Rocks like <u>granite</u> have a high background count.

3) Certain <u>underground rocks</u> can cause higher levels at the <u>surface</u>, especially if they release <u>radioactive radon gas</u>, which tends to get trapped <u>inside</u> people's houses. This varies widely across the UK depending on the <u>rock type</u>, as shown.

Radiation Harms Living Cells

1) <u>Alpha</u>, <u>beta</u> and <u>gamma</u> radiation enter living cells and <u>collide</u> with molecules.

2) These collisions cause <u>ionisation</u>, which <u>damages</u> or <u>destroys</u> the molecules.

3) <u>Lower</u> doses tend to cause <u>minor</u> damage without <u>killing</u> the cell.

4) This can give rise to <u>mutant</u> cells which divide <u>uncontrollably</u>. This is <u>cancer</u>.

5) <u>Higher</u> doses tend to <u>kill cells</u> completely, which causes <u>radiation sickness</u> if a lot of your body cells all get <u>blatted at once</u>.

6) The <u>extent</u> of the harmful effects depends on <u>two</u> things:

a) How much <u>exposure</u> you have to the radiation.

b) The <u>energy</u> and <u>penetration</u> of the radiation emitted, since some types are more <u>hazardous</u> than others, of course.

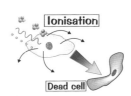

radiation hits nucleus

damaged cell

cancer

Ionisation

Dead cell

Disposing of Radioactive Waste

<u>Radioactive waste</u> is a problem because it can take a <u>long time</u> to become safe.

1) Low level waste is <u>weak</u> radioactive material. It is <u>buried</u> at special sites, or <u>released</u> into the environment (but there are strict guidelines for this).

2) High level waste from nuclear power plants is <u>highly radioactive</u> and dangerous, and mainly <u>stored</u> in special tanks. The tanks are <u>cooled</u> because the radiation generates <u>heat</u>.

3) Some high level waste is turned into a <u>glass-like</u> material, and stored in cooled stainless steel containers.

4) It can take <u>years</u> for the radiation to fall to <u>safe</u> levels.

Background Radiation — it's no good burying your head in the sand...

Radiation is zapping us all of the time — quite a scary thought really. Know the <u>three</u> places where background radiation comes from, and <u>what it does</u> when it hits us, and then write a <u>mini-essay</u> to see what you know. Don't give up — <u>keep going</u> until you can remember it all.

Revision Summary for Module Six

One thing's for sure — there are loads of fairly easy facts to learn about waves and radioactivity. Of course there are still some bits which need thinking about, but really, most of it is fairly easy stuff which just needs learning. Don't forget, this book contains all the important information which they've specifically mentioned in the syllabus, and this is precisely the stuff they're going to test you on in the Exams. You must practise these questions over and over again until they're easy.

1) Sketch a) a transverse wave, b) a longitudinal wave. Give an example of each.

2) Define frequency, amplitude and wavelength for a wave and label the last two on a sketch.

3) Describe two effects of waves that show waves carry energy.

4) Draw a sketch of the EM spectrum showing all its details.

5) Give details of the uses of radio waves, microwaves and infrared radiation.

6) Which aspect of EM waves determines their differing properties?

7) Detail one use of X-rays, and two uses of UV light and gamma rays, and say how harmful different dosages are.

8) What is refraction? What causes it? How does it affect wavelength and frequency?

9) Sketch a ray of light going through a rectangular glass block, showing the angles i and r. What if i=90°?

10) Describe total internal reflection. When does it occur?

11) Explain the differences between analogue and digital signals.

12) Why do signals have to be amplified? Why are digital signals better quality?

13) Give details of the two main uses of optical fibres. How do optical fibres work?

14) What is ultrasound? Give details of two applications of ultrasound.

15) List the planets in order. How do we see them?

16) What force keeps the stars in a galaxy together? What galaxy are we in?

17) Why are comets only visible from Earth every few years?

18) What is the relationship between the gravitational force between two masses and the distance between them?

19) Give a detailed description of the life cycle of a small star.

20) What are the arguments against the Steady State Theory?

21) Explain briefly the Big Bang Theory of the Universe, and the evidence supporting it.

22) Describe the possible fates of the Universe.

23) What does SETI stand for? What exactly is SETI?

24) Explain what the mass number and atomic number of an atom represent.

25) Write down the number of electrons, protons and neutrons there are in an atom of $^{226}_{88}$Ra.

26) Explain what isotopes are. Give an example.

27) Radioactive decay is a totally random process. Explain what this means.

28) Describe in detail the nature and properties of the three types of radiation: α, β, and γ.

29) How do the three types compare in penetrating power and ionising power? What blocks them?

30) Describe in detail how radioactive isotopes are used in each of the following:
    a) sterilising food, b) smoke alarms, c) thickness control.

31) List three places where the level of background radiation is increased and explain why.

32) What damage does a high dose of radiation cause to body cells?

Index

Index

Index